The Music of Ghosts

PJ Curtis

Photos by
Mike Mulcaire

Old Forge Books

ALSO BY AUTHOR

Non-Fiction
Notes From The Heart – A Celebration of
Irish Traditional Music (Poolbeg 1994)

Fiction
One Night In The Life Of R.V. Mulrooney (Poolbeg 1996)
The Lightning Tree (Brandon Books 2006)

Dedicated to the memory
of my late father and mother,
Pat Joe and Sarah Curtis.

Also to the memory of
Cyril Ó Céirín (1935-1999)
(Writer, Poet, Painter, Philosopher, Scholar
and Warrior Environmentalist)
I was proud to call him a friend.

Published in 2003
Reprinted 2007

Old Forge Books
The Old Forge,
Kilnaboy,
Co. Clare,
Rep. Of Ireland.

Contact pjc1@eircom.net
© PJ Curtis 2003

ISBN 0-9545365-0-9

All photos and front and back cover by Mike Mulcaire © 2003

Design and layout by Pat Pidgeon

Printed by Lightning Source UK Ltd.
www.lightningsource.com

Acknowledgments

The encouragement, support and friendship of so many people over the years saw me through the writing of this collection of essays, stories and poems.

Special thanks to the following people:

To Kit Ó Céirín and Eddie Stack for their wise words of advice and especially to Pat Musick (Colorado) whose unswerving friendship, inspiration and mentorship I greatly value.

To my sister Mary Moroney, to Leo & Claire Hallisey, to Josephine Marsh, Gaye Shortland, Dermot & Carole Reidy, Cormac & Annette McConnell, Phil Cousineau (San Fran.), Cindy Reich (Colorado), Maribeth Gus (Idaho), Mary Beth Noonan (Mass), Carol Langstaff & Jim Rooney (Vermont and E. Galway), Kyle and Sue Harris (Ariz.), Libby Symon & Fergus Kinmonth (London and Clare), Kathy Donahey (N. Mex), Tim Collins (U.C.G.), Sr. Kathleen McGrath (Aust.), Anne Jones, Ray Conway, Alice Lawless, John Keane, Edel Butler and all the members of the Burren Action Group.

Also a special 'thank you' to my editor Brian Richardson, to Harry Hughes (Ed. Dal gCais), Letitia Pollard (Ed. Ireland of the Welcomes), Martina Scanlon & Gerry Collison (Ed. The Clare Champion), Sean Spellissy, Paddy Pidgeon for cover and page layout and to Mike Mulcaire, whose magical photos grace the cover and these pages and go beyond the power of words.

A sincere 'thank you' to one and all.

Contents

A Burren miscellany: Recollections, memories and reflections on growing up in North Clare in the 1950's

Part 1

The Road of Souls

The Road of Souls

*"Memory is not which we remember
but that which remembers us.
Memory is a present that never stops passing".*
Octavio Paz

I'M AT THE AGE WHEN MEMORY BEGINS TO FAIL me. I've always prided myself in having a sharp memory; being instantly able to recall - with total clarity, down to the smallest details - names, faces, events. Indeed I once had the ability to recall any event or scene from all the days and decades of my past. Now when memories come, they are sometimes reluctant and ragged; presenting themselves like tired, grey ghosts, each one irritated at being awakened and summoned from that amorphous, chaotic shifting of directionless mass, which now passes for my darkening pool of memory. But I suppose Mother Nature knows what's best and perhaps not every memory is worth keeping.

The memories, which come easiest, now are those from earlier parts of my life and will often leap unbidden to my mind with greater clarity than events from last week, or even yesterday. I don't understand why that is so, but this is the way of memory. Memory, it seems to me, lives by its own, separate and immutable rules.

Often, the sweetest, though sometimes more painful, recollections are triggered by a simple casual word, a familiar sound and sometimes even a particular taste or scent.

On one particular evening in late Autumn, it was a combination of all those things – a distant dog barking in the frosty night air, the sweet, wafting aroma of a hazel-wood fire from a nearby chimney and the sharp, cold twinkling of a solitary star in the northern sky. Sitting alone in my kitchen, with the clock ticking off the minutes, I had the urge to breathe in the bracing autumn night air. I stepped outside and looked skyward. Suddenly, without warning, I was propelled back down the time-tunnel of memory. In the turn of that moment, I was once again ten years old and sitting by the campfire of old Rory Dubh, 'Black Rory' the Traveller; the Last Prince of Thomond.

It's different now. These days, Travelling People are greeted mostly either with suspicion or outright aggression and hostility. It was not always so. There was always a welcome extended to Travellers who called at our door and the doors of our neighbours. In those days, they were never called 'Travellers' they were known only as 'Tinkers'. Only Rory Dubh commanded the title of 'Traveller', setting him apart from others of his wandering, dispossessed tribe.

"They're the true Irish," my father told us. "They were once well-to-do landowners and free-holders driven off their rightful lands and properties by Oliver Cromwell and his cursed armies, and forced to take to the roads of Ireland as a way of life."

They were, my father explained, the great Clan of the Dispossessed, traversing for generations the highways and byways and following the four seasons and their rambling instincts to the traditional camping grounds.

We knew most of these Travelling families by name – The MacDonaghs, The Sherlocks, the Fureys – and they arrived and departed with the seasons and the waxing and waning of the moons.

"The Tinkers are coming! The Tinkers are coming!" I was more excited at the coming of the Tinkers than if they were the Circus. We children would shout with glee as my brothers and I would run to witness their arrival. Looking, for all the world, like a cross between a tribe of Plains Indians and a frontier wagon-train, they trouped by our house to set-up camp on one of their traditional sheltered halting sites nearby.

I would follow the carts and gaily-painted caravans at a distance to observe the bustling activity. From a safe distance, I watched in fascination as the black-shawled women set equally blackened pots over hastily prepared cooking-fires arranged at the centre of the camp. Meanwhile, the swarthy, black-haired tinker-men busied themselves erecting tents over arched hazel-boughs to the laughter of barefoot, wild-eyed children who – wild and free – ran hither and thither, the bleating of goats and the yelping of fierce looking mongrel dogs. Nearby, their unfettered piebald ponies and donkeys – as a reward for their long day's labours – were loosed to chomp the sweet roadside grass, shrubs and blossoms or stray into nearby private pastures.

Sometimes they would see me and wave and shyly I would return the greeting from a distance.

The arrival of the Tinkers was always something to look forward to, a whirl of excitement to spice the humdrum routine of daily life. Not so the appearance of the lone, dark-featured Travelling man whom sometimes showed up to our door, usually without warning. This man we feared. We feared his aloneness; we feared the two brooding dogs seated on his red-wheeled cart, which was drawn by a tired, scraggy old pony. We feared his sudden, silent arrivals and departures and most of all, we feared the deep-set, sullen, darting eyes which flashed from his weather-beaten, threatening face.

I cannot recall the first time I laid eyes on Rory 'Dubh' O'Brien, but do remember, as a small boy, scurrying like a frightened rabbit to the safety of my bedroom on his arrival at our door. The very mention of his name sent a shiver of fear down my spine.

"If you misbehave," my mother warned us whenever our childish high-jinx threatened to get out of hand. "I'll give you to Rory Dubh, who will put you in his sack and take you away with him."

The sight of Rory Dubh on his cart arriving in our farm-yard, when the first November frosts pinched our noses and fingers, would immediately send us scampering to the safety of a bedroom closet or underneath a bed to await his departure. So hidden, we would remain out of sight in case mother should decide to carry out her threat. From our secure hiding places, we would hear Rory Dubh thump the kitchen floor with his blackthorn stick, chuckle loudly and in a loud voice ask my mother, "Any bold or troublesome childer' to give away today, missus?"

We hardly dare breath as we listened to mother assuring him that there were no bad children in this house. Deciding to be on the safe side, we remained frozen in our hideaway havens, tingling and giggling both in fear and in fascination.

We knew well of course that Rory Dubh would soon depart, as

he always did, and with nothing more in that mysterious old canvas bag of his than the loose vegetables, fresh baked soda-bread, milk and cuts of meat given him by my mother. Only then would we come, tumbling and shrieking with laughter – and not to mention a great sense of relief – from our hiding places. We would later admit, of course, that we never doubted for a minute that this was but a game; played for the adults pleasure and entertainment, as much as it was for us. Nevertheless, we thought it best to play it safe, as there was always the possibility that we might – just might – end up inside of Rory Dubh's grubby old canvas sack.

Time passed and we came to no longer fear, as we once did, the strange, silent Traveller who came to our door.

"He's the last of his kind. He's the last of the Princes of Thomond." My Father often said. He would tell us about Rory Dubh's aristocratic O'Brien clan whose ancestors once ruled over half the province as kings, princes and chieftains. I listened in amazement and tried to understand that this ragged old man with skin like burnt parchment could in fact be a wandering and deposed king or prince or even a chieftain. It seemed unbelievable to me, but I could tell from the way that my father spoke of him – and in his conversations with him- that he held Rory Dubh in very high esteem indeed. Sometimes, as I hid from the dark Traveller, I would peek out and see my father seated with Rory Dubh on the wall at the far end of the farmyard, both smoking pipes and idly chatting. I remember being both confused and angry that my father could banter so lightly with the man who threatened to carry us away with him.

As time passed, I learned just how much my father actually looked forward to Rory Dubh's spring and autumn visits and conversing with the old man. In between times, Rory Dubh, along with his dogs and pony and cart, was a familiar sight to all as he travelled through the lands once held by his royal ancestors. What thoughts passed through his mind as his cart trundled by the walls of the now-deserted fortresses and castles? – inside which his Clan forebears once sat down to Councils of War and victory feasts.

When Rory Dubh arrived at last in our farmyard my father would rush to warmly greet him. When both men sat down together, the talk would be of strange, new places Rory had visited and the many people he had encountered since last he was here. From all over the county – and beyond – he brought fresh news of betrothals, weddings and births, of illnesses and deaths; of horse, sheep and cattle-fairs, of football and hurling matches, of house-céilís, crossroads dances and faction fights. He repeated with relish – and more than likely exaggerated – the pronouncements of politicians, priests, publicans and postmen he had encountered on his journeys. He retold the idle gossip of farm-wife and fishwife and he regaled us with tall-tales as told to him as 'gospel truth' by drunkard and simpleton. He reported on potato, wheat and barley yields, on cattle and sheep prices, with the same attention to detail as he relayed the gossip, the rumours and whispers, the hard-news and hear-say he had gleaned from his many sources and informants in the far-flung hamlets and villages and the back-roads and byways along his meandering route.

"The man is as good as the Sunday Press . . . or The Clare Champion!" My father would declare with delight, after Rory Dubh's bi-annual visits. "I learn more from him in half-an-hour than I do from either newspaper in a week."

One sharp, frosty November evening as darkness fell, I passed close to the site where Rory Dubh traditionally made his camp for the night. From a distance, the perfume of his hazel-wood fire wafted gently on the still air. The yellow glow from his campfire looked as a fallen star. In the half-light, he recognised me and called out for me to join him.

I approached the camp with caution. After all, this was the same man who, not too many years before, had filled my siblings and I with such dread and fear. From beneath the cart, his two mongrel dogs eyed me with suspicion as I moved closer. But I was utterly intrigued by the man, by his fierce aura of independence; his cool, secure aloofness and most of all; I was fascinated by his aura of serenity and royal mystery. I was, I had to admit, very much in awe of this ragged old travelling man, this Prince of his tribe – maybe a King even! – who now summoned me to his camp-fire-court. He motioned me to take a seat, pointing at an up-turned butter-box by the fire while he sat, a clay-pipe protruding from his remaining, uneven teeth, between the shafts of his cart. His dark, hooded eyes never left me as I slowly and nervously moved within the circle of dancing, amber firelight and settled myself on the upturned timber box.

He smiled a slow smile as I accepted the tin mug of hot, sweet tea, which he poured from the Billycan boiling on the glowing-red embers. He had many questions; all of which I shyly tried to answer. What age was I now? Did I like school? Was I good at lessons? Did I read books?

"Books are better for you than bread." Rory Dubh said, puffing hard at his clay-pipe and stirring the fire with his blackthorn stick. The fire blazed and hissed and spat as if angry at being disturbed. I sipped my tea and stared in to the crackling coals.

After a long silence, he pointed his stick upwards.

"There's my book." He said softly. "The book of the sky." My eyes followed the stick from the glowing embers to the glowing star-spangled heavens. "Every night, a different page. Every page, a different story to tell."

Together we gazed deep into the frosty night air.

"Do you know anything at all about stars?" he turned to me, his eyes as bright as the hazel-stick embers. I shook my head and continued to gaze up and the carpet of diamond-hard stars twinkling overhead.

"There's the Great Bear . . . there's the Plow . . . there's the Seven Sisters, surrounded by their clans . . . and there's the North Star . . . the traveller's friend . . . but there . . ." he swept his arm in a wide arc, "is the Milky way . . . the mighty Milky Way!"

My eyes followed the wide sweep of his arm.

"Do you know what it's made up of?"

I shook my head again.

"Souls." He said softly. "The souls of the dead."

His words chilled me to the bone and seemed to send a shiver through the arc of stars like a soft wind stirring wind chimes.

His voice sounded far away as he continued. "When we die, our souls fly up there to join all those who have gone before us and get in line to enter Heaven. Every star you see is a soul waiting its turn to go through the Gates of Paradise."

I stared at the great trail of shimmering light across the canopy of the heavens and tried to imagine how many millions of souls went to make up this vast highway in the night sky.

"Every time we see a star fall to earth, it's another soul allowed into heaven." Rory Dubh spoke so softly now his voice was but a brittle whisper and I knew he spoke only to himself. "We're all heading for a place on that road of souls. All my own people are gone on ahead and they're up there now, waiting for me to join them."

His old eyes scanned the flight of stars.

"I'll be there alot sooner than you, young fella!" He jabbed his stick at me across the blazing sticks and twigs. He looked upwards again and added. "And the better we are on this journey here below, the brighter our souls will glow on that journey above."

Rory Dubh grinned a rotten-tooth grin and added. "I'm sure you'll make a grand bright star . . . but not for a good long time yet with the help of the Man above!"

We sipped the sweet tea and lapsed into silent communion. The night had deepened and fire now cast dancing shadows on the nearby stones and whitethorn bushes and its sparks seemed to jump directly into the Milky Way to join that shining throng on their eternal journey.

Rory Dubh turned his face again toward the sky and for a long while I watched the glow of the firelight and the years etched on his old, weatherworn features. When he looked at me again across the campfire I saw in his eyes – a moment ago reflecting the twinkling of distant stars – the glistening of a tear.

"Every journey we make on this old earth is but in preparation for the longer journey which awaits us all. We're all on our own separate journeys . . . prince or priest or pauper . . . each on his own road . . . and there is no road without bends."

Rory Dubh sighed, smiled a slow, secret smile, then reached inside his canvas sack from which he drew a brown-paper package and said gently, "Would you like a piece of rhubarb cake? It's your mother's baking. Your mother makes the finest tarts in the whole county. I've never tasted better."

I wanted to say 'yes', but refused. He sighed again, nodded his royal head and retreated further inside his black tattered, greatcoat. He rubbed his mittened hands together and turned them towards the dancing flames. "It's going to be a long cold night . . . maybe you had better be off home with you yourself, young fella. Your mother won't thank me if you catch you death sitting out under such a hard frost as this . . . so off with you now!"

He reached out to stroke the neck of the tired old pony tethered to the wheel of his cart. "Old Jenny and myself have a long road ahead of us tomorrow and we'll be needing our rest."

Reluctantly, I said my shy goodbyes and left Rory Dubh's camp to make my way home. As I slowly walked away from the circle of light and heat, my imagination raced, my head full of sky and stars. A cold November moon had risen in the east and sat for a moment on the far horizon while its pale light turned the hazel and whitethorn trees to ghosts and the stones to gold. There was magic in the night air and I breathed deeply of it.

As I walked away, I could hear behind me the old man singing quietly and gently to himself, his pony and his dogs.

In the sharp night air his voice floated clear and lonesome:
"Oh well I do remember the bleak December Day.
That landlord and the sheriff came to drive us all away.
They set my roof on fire with their cursed English spleen.
And that's another reason I left old Skibereeen."

I never saw Rory Dubh alive again.

Later that same night, warm and secure by my own fireside, Rory Dubh filled my thoughts and I longed to be back with him at his campfire, peering deep into that starry road of souls.

I arose early next morning and returned to his campsite to see him again, to bid him farewell on his journeys and give him a gift of a pot of my mother's homemade gooseberry jam.

But Rory Dubh the Traveller, along with Jenny, his pony and his two dogs, had moved on. How different things looked to me in the cold morning light. The campsite now looked strangely forlorn and abandoned. The only sign of Rory Dubh's overnight stay were the ruts cut into the frosted earth by his cart-wheels and all that remained of the magic and majesty of his royal court of the previous night, were a few still-smouldering embers among the cold ash within the fire's stone circle.

Time passed and there was no further word on Rory Dubh or his whereabouts. Then came the day in the spring of the following year that we got the news that Rory Dubh the Traveller – last Prince of Thomond – was dead. He had been found underneath his cart one freezing January morning; his frost-covered remains being watched over and waked by his trusty old pony and faithful dogs. They said his wake was attended by hundreds of Travellers from three counties and he was at last laid to rest in an unmarked pauper's grave in an ancient graveyard nearby the road so he could hear the Traveller's cart and caravans go by when spring and autumn came again.

That night I went outside to catch a glimpse of the Milky Way and whisper a prayer for the soul of Rory Dubh O'Brien – that gentle roadside emperor and descendant of kings.

My memory is not as sharp as it once was, but tonight as I catch the scent of a Hazelwood fire, hear a dog baying somewhere in the distance and look skyward at that splash of light painted across the moonless night-sky, I shed a tear for both myself and for Rory Dubh the Traveller.

I fancy now I see his Star light up the Milky Way. It twinkles brighter than all the rest, as he makes camp, reunited at last with his own people on his final journey along that endless road of Souls.

The long years that have separated him and I grow heavy on my shoulders and it probably won't be too long before I set off down that same starry road on my own last journey.

How I long to sit again with Rory Dubh; to warm my hands by his campfire and watch it cast long shadows which dance across the universe; to drink again his sweet tea; to gaze again into his wise old eyes and outward into space, to other lights and other stars . . . and remember.

The Sorcerer's Apprentice

(Winner of the 2000 IRMA Essay Award, Muskoka, Canada)

I REMEMBER READING SOMEWHERE OF THE infinite number of possibilities open to us as we make the often-precarious journey from the cradle to the grave; that each conscious moment offers us a choice. But what different lives we might have lived – if only we had seized that golden opportunity or grasped that quicksilver moment.

"If only . . . if only . . . " how often have we uttered those words, those bittersweet darts of longing and regret. For myself one of those choices was made, and a possibility cast carelessly aside on a winter's day long, long ago. I had accompanied my father to a small farm deep in the Burren in North Clare, where the farmer's horse was dying of a disease called Farcee. While I cannot recall the farmer's name or face, the day's main events are etched in my memory forever.

I was eight years old in 1952. I was born in the latter days of the war in the ancient and historic townland of Kilnaboy at the southern edge of the Burren, in Co Clare. These were the final years of living daily life without electricity, indoor toilet or bathroom, and for the great majority of people living in Rural Ireland, living without any form of motorised transport. In those days you could count on one hand the number of motorcars to be seen on the un-tarred and gravel-packed roads of North Clare in any one week. It was an unchanged and unchanging world. A world where the past intertwined with the present. A world populated with ghosts and spirits and superstitions. It was a world of cooking over peat-turf fires; of low, gentle conversation or story-telling by flickering oil-lamp or candlelight on long winter nights; and running barefoot through the dew-wet grass in fragrant May. A world where every man, woman and child moved to the ageless rhythm, pulse and magic of the seasons.

It was also a world without television (an undreamed of luxury) and few people possessed a radio. More significantly though, the fifties signaled the end of the 'Age of the Horse' in rural Ireland.

For generations, the horse was the farmer's most prized possession. A horse to plough, to sow and to mow; to draw home the harvest and transport livestock to fairs and markets and almost daily to bring the family in 'common-cars' and carts, sidecars and traps to town fairs and village shops and to church for baptisms, weddings and funerals. As time passed, however, the working horse was eventually replaced in almost every household and farm with the tractor and motorcar.

I miss the horse from the landscape; and I can still hear the sweet music of the clop of well-shod hooves; the creak of oiled, gleaming harness and the graunch of cartwheel on the unpaved, graveled roads.

My father, whose family had lived in North Clare since 1700, made his living in two ways. Firstly, he farmed a smallholding – as had his forebears – fighting the seasonal battles of small farmers in the bleak post-war economic landscape that was Ireland in the forties and fifties. This was the Ireland of the ration book, Ireland of mass labour migration and ever-deepening economic depression with no State handouts. These were lean and difficult times for everybody, yet I don't recall any one of us ever being in need or going hungry.

My father was also a Blacksmith, the only one for miles around and when he wasn't in the fields he could be found at work behind his anvil forging horse-shoes from lathes of iron for seemingly endless queues of horses. He came from a long line of Blacksmiths and there was a working forge in our farmyard going back many generations. A number of Pike (spear) heads in our house were made by one of my ancestors in the forge in preparation for the 1798 Rising.

For most people back then, material possessions were few and basic, while luxuries of any kind were even more rare. Looking back, I see now that my father positively shunned the acquisition of wealth for wealth's sake. He did however possess something so rare and so special, that now, almost twenty years after his death, aged eighty, old men who farmed in west and north Clare and in south Galway still speak of him and his special talent – his special 'Gift'.

My father was a Healer. He possessed what the locals referred to as the 'Charm' or 'The Cure'.

This gift of healing was not something my father picked up by chance; it was inherited. He was the only male survivor, having lost his three elder brothers, a sister and his mother, to TB during 1918-20, while still in his teens. So as the only surviving boy, the 'Cure', and all that it entailed, was passed down to him by my grandfather; who himself had received it from his father, and so on, back through the generations for hundreds of years.

So where did this 'gift' – this healing power – come from?

The story went that, several generations earlier in Penal times, a priest, in flight from his English pursuers, had stopped by our forge and begged for help. My ancestor came to his aid by removing the horse's shoes and replacing them back to front; thus sending his trackers on a false trail. In return, so the story went, that the grateful priest gave the powers of healing to the quick-thinking smithy. But the knowledge was more ancient, more arcane than anybody living could determine.

Another branch of the family, who lived nearby, also possessed healing powers. The difference between their family and ours was that they had the 'Cure' for humans while our family possessed the 'Cure' for animals – especially horses. For as long as anybody could remember, whenever a horse went down with the Colic, the Gripe, Hoof-rot, lameness, Farcee or any of the ills that might befall an animal, the owner would beat a path to our door for help. And help was always on hand.

My father never refused a request to visit a sick horse; no matter how far the journey or what other work he had on hand at the time.

One old man once told me, "Pat Joe Curtis could bring a horse back from its last gasp. Even when the Vet advised that the animal was beyond help and should be put down, your father was always called for. He would put the 'Cure' on the beast and after a month or two that animal would be ploughing or mowing!"

Restoring a horse seemingly beyond hope to full health was something he achieved more that once. We grew up with all this so, naturally, we did not give a second thought to callers to the house at all hours asking my father to go off with them to visit yet another sick animal. He never accepted any money for his services; yet he never returned home empty-handed. In earnest gratitude, farmers always presented him with bags of fresh vegetables, choice cuts of mutton, home-cured bacon and ham, chickens, geese and more than once he returned home with the odd bottle of the highest quality Poteen.

As I was the eldest, my father began to take me with him to attend sick horses, almost always in a hired hackney car for long journeys, as we didn't own a car. I relished every opportunity to travel away from home to exotic places like Bellharbour and Galway Bay and to Spanish Point and the wild Atlantic. It was always a great and exciting day out; filled with new sights, sounds and scents. On arrival at the farmyard, I would be taken into the kitchen – and treated to cool home-made lemonade in Summer or, in Winter, to large mugs of hot, sweet tea and rhubarb or apple tarts or buns – while my father attended to the sick horse. Afterwards, a smiling farmer (happy in the knowledge that his sick animal would soon be back in full health and in harness) would drop a coin or two in my pocket before we departed for home.

Not too many of these outings went by before it was made very clear to me by my father that I was to ". . . pay close attention to everything he did and everything he said . . ." while attending a sick horse. Of course, I didn't realise it at the time, but I was being tutored in the Healing Arts so that I could carry on the family tradition: Pat Joe's apprentice. This, however, was never to be; something I will regret to my dying day.

"Pay good attention to me and you'll soon get the gist of it. It's all only common sense." He would say. The Cure had come down through the generations and now was to be passed to me, the eldest son. There was much to learn about healing and about the horse, a magnificent animal. I was to learn about its individual physical traits and personality, and its varied illnesses.

"Never look on a horse as a dumb animal." My father would say. "They are more intelligent and more aware than ninety percent of their owners! They can see and sense things that we can't. Never forget that."

He would recite, as one long poem, the litanies of potions, washes and ointments and the even longer litanies of exotic ingredients that went into the careful preparation, for the Cure. To me, their strange-sounding names were as magic spells, carrying powers beyond my wildest dreams and imaginings. One such cure, which he boiled to a sticky blue-black glue in a special skillet-pot before applying it as a kind of Plaster-of-Paris to an animal's broken back or leg bones, consisted of no less than twelve ingredients.

He would recite:
"Black Pitch, Burgundy Pitch,
Venus Turpentine, Resin,
Beeswax, Mastic,
Diaclin, Armenian Bowl,
Oxacrotia, Euphorbium,
Cantardes and Corrosive Sublimate.
Twelve ingredients. Remember them as you would the names of the twelve Apostles."

This was easier said than done, Apostles names were at least pronounceable! And how I struggled to learn by heart these strange-sounding, magical names that held so much power for my father.

Another healing cure-mixture contained such elements as Tincture of Myrrh, Oil of Cloves, Sulphate of Lead and a mystery element, which he called 'Woundstone'. No present-day chemist can say just what 'Woundstone' is. All the other mixtures and cures are now lost or forgotten.

The 'Catching of the Blood' was to be my introduction to the role of Healer's Apprentice. From the beginning, it was not a task I particularly relished. I had a problem with the sight of blood and I still get squeamish at the sight of any blood-human or animal.

"When I strike the Lance with the stick," my father would sternly instruct me, "you catch the blood in this jar . . . and don't spill a drop no matter what the horse does." I timidly tried to do as he instructed me. The bleeding of the horse was an essential part of the cure for Farcee, a disease that, if left untreated, usually proved fatal. I took my task seriously and, like Mickey Mouse in Disney's 'Fantasia', I played the bumbling Apprentice to my father's 'Sorcerer'.

On the face of it, the ritual of the Cure seemed straightforward enough. Pat Joe always seemed to know how the animal would respond and if it could be cured. From the moment he laid his hands on a sick horse (more than other animals, horses especially seemed to respond to his gifts) there always was a positive outcome.

From the moment he stepped close to the animal, his concentration and focus was total. His gaze would lock with that of the animal, all the while speaking to it in a gentle, mantra-like whisper. This had the most extraordinary calming effect on the stricken animal. Once he had moved close enough to lay hands on the horse's head, it became further gentled and peaceful as he continued for a long while to stroke its neck and whisper in its ear.

This examination complete, if the horse suffered from the life-threatening Farcee, he would then make preparations to bleed the animal which entailed drawing several pints of blood from the horse's jugular vein and leaving it undisturbed to settle. My father would then inspect the blood and, according to its ratio to serum, he would administer his specially prepared concoction. The dose complete, he would instruct the farmer as to further treatment. He rarely, if ever, had to make a second visit.

One sharp, frosty November day in 1952, my father was called to attend a horse with Farcee. As usual, I was to assist. The animal was a huge farm-horse; standing 18 hands high. I remember it, eyes showing white with fear and pain, ears pinned back and towering above this nervous eight-year-old clutching a 2-lb. jam-jar in which to catch the blood.

"Easy girl . . . easy girl . . ." my father whispered while he stroked the horse's face and neck, before clipping away the hair from the chosen pressure-point on the jugular-vein. "Here's the spot, watch it pulse," he said quietly to me before placing the sharp-edged lance-blade called a 'fleam' – a small pocket knife with a half-moon blade projection – on the shaven, throbbing vein. He always carried the same well-used, brown lancing-stick and now he brought it down quickly and deftly on the placed lance. The blow, when delivered, had to be precise. Hard, sharp and skillful enough to pierce skin and vein, though not so as to cut through the jugular; which would, of course, be fatal for the animal.

I was always amazed at the force of the dark blood as it flowed thick and pungent from the horse's neck. I raised the jar to catch the blood and as I did, the horse reared backwards, reacting to the sting of the lance-blow. Instead of catching the stream of blood in the outstretched jar, my face and neck took the full rush of the flow. Blinded, I panicked and backed away.

"Stand still! Hold your ground!" My father snapped at both the horse and me. He "shushed" repeatedly to calm the prancing horse while the animal's dark blood poured in sticky rivers down my face and neck, my eyes and tongue smarting. I obeyed my father's command – as did the horse – and stood my ground. Once more, spitting and blinking, I held the jar aloft toward the wildly spraying blood in a desperate effort to capture enough to satisfy my father's needs. I suppose I must have succeeded, but all I remember was nausea and nameless fear. In that moment, I knew that there was one thing I could never be, a Horse Doctor!

Memories of the rest of the day are sketchy and vague. I watched my father pluck a hair from the horse's tail-mane before laying it on the bloody wound, to help the process of natural healing.

Later, inside the warm farmhouse kitchen, as my father and the farmer sipped whiskey or something stronger, I suppose I must have received the usual treat of tea and fresh-baked cake from the farmer's wife and I may have been given a shilling from the farmer as we left. On the journey home, my father, aware of my distress may have given me praise for my work.

I do however, remember that night, when I awoke from a nightmare so real and terrifying that its vivid details shake me still, over forty-five years later. I awoke in a terrified state; drenched in sweat and thinking it horse-blood, as I smelled again the pungent stench and tasted again the thick, sour horse-blood in the darkness of my bedroom. I lay awake for a long while – the dream images still swirling through my mind. For a long time afterwards, I dreaded sleep and the return of the nightmare.

I have no recollection of ever accompanying my father on any of his curing trips again. He didn't press me for a reason and eventually stopped asking me. As I never completed my 'Apprenticeship', I never learned my father's healing arts; which were my rightful inheritance. What arcane knowledge my father possessed, he took with him to the grave. I can only guess how different my life might have been had I absorbed that ancient lore. If only things had turned out differently that day. I realise now that, I had unwittingly lost a unique chance of acquiring a priceless knowledge. Moreover, a chain had been broken, a bond severed and, as I know now, I also lost my father. He must have known too that he had lost me to a nameless fear, which I could never articulate to him, or fully understand myself. Later, I was lost to a world that was -in the fifties and sixties – invading his old world and destroying it.

I can only guess at my father's feelings and his growing sense of bewilderment as he watched me embrace this 'new world'; this brash, alien, fast-changing world he scarcely understood and which was about to sweep away entirely the old values and the old ways.

In very few years, the horse had almost disappeared – as a working animal – from the landscape. College-trained men in white coats and leather cases brim-full of high-priced tablets and pills of every size and colour were now treating those horses who did survive – whether ailing, sick or wounded. The world was now in the hands of those who had little or no tolerance, or belief, in the rural, untrained 'horse-doctor'; with their murky bottles and potions, natural roots and herbs and most of all, their mysterious, whispered incantations.

It was only following his death that I came to learn the true nature of the rare talent my father possessed and by his death I came to understand the wealth of the inheritance he had offered and the ancient family tradition that I had failed to continue.

Neither of my two younger brothers or my sister took up this old knowledge from him. We had severed, unknowingly, a chain of knowledge that stretched in an unbroken line through several generations.

If only . . . if only.

The Plough

By a briary hedgerow lying,
I see a plough,
forgotten.
Its iron-brown bones,
stark and weed-adorned,
point accusingly
at this unforgiving age.

I saw it once slice
secrets, black and brittle,
from the warm grape of earth.
True and firm, it rode
the emerald waves
and it seemed to surge
with power and life,
between sinewy arm
and straining beast.

What piercing, graceful
action then,
man to plough to horse.
Shiva's Dance enacted,
as harvest's promise pour
from a sweat-sweetened soil.
Three proud masters these,
at Spring's eternal labours.

Gone is the Plowman now from the land.
Gone with summer days
that creaked with well-oiled leather
and foaming horse-bits.

Man and beast
to the giving womb
of the earth which poured them forth.

Now lies the plough,
cast up, adrift
on the naked shore
of this machine-raped land.
Tricked by Time and circumstance,
even oblivion's promise denied.
Yet it listens
for the imperious pulse of Spring.

A Day in The Forge

THE CLEAR, RHYTHMIC 'CLANG' OF HAMMER on iron; of steel on steel; the deep-bell tone of resonating anvil; the arcing, spitting and fiery showering of sparks; the pungent aroma of sweat and burning horse-hoof, the fierce hiss and sizzle of red-hot metal being plunged into a stone-trough of iron-brown water; the stamping of horse hooves on a cobblestone floor and the snorting and bit-chomping of an impatient animal.

These are sounds and smells I remember: a backdrop to men conversing; sometimes in hushed whispers, sometimes loudly and punctuated often by raucous laughter from deep within this old stone-wall building.

For a small boy, the whole effect created a strange, complex and fascinating melody. This was the music, a symphony of vibrant sound emanating from some hidden and unknown orchestra, that initially draws me towards this place – the old Forge which stood for almost two centuries in our farmyard.

I am two or three years of age and I reluctantly retreat to stand out of harm's way some distance from the Forge door; my father, having seen me pull playfully at the tail of a waiting horse, 'shoos' me away to a safe distance.

"Get yourself to a safe spot." He chides. "You'll get trampled to smithereens if you sit around under horse's legs."

Reluctantly I move beyond the circle of danger. But never too far from the action as I am already fascinated at the daily goings-on within this place that my father inhabits from morning till night and for most of the working week when not working in the fields.

After a while I drift slowly back towards the Forge door to yet again peek inside this dark cauldron of smoke and sound, of animal and human activity and of strange exotic aromas. For a small boy who, as yet, saw no danger in wanting to handle shards of red-hot iron, grabbing swishing horsetails or crawling under the hooves of excitable horses, this was a place of fascination and of possible play and excitement.

But the old Forge, with all its dark, shadowy corners and hidden secrets was, I soon learned, a place of many dangers; a forbidden place where only adult men (even my mother never entered here) conducted some strange ritual on a daily basis. Even as a toddler, I realised that whatever was being transacted within these low stone walls was, as yet, outside my understanding.

But I was determined to find out and enter into that grown-up world of noise and activity.

My father was a Blacksmith; his father before him was a Blacksmith and his father before him was a Blacksmith. Indeed it would seem that the family had been involved in the 'smithy' trade for as far back as memory could hold and even further back. They were Blacksmiths and horse-lovers and carers of animals when they arrived in the county and to the Burren in the mid 1500's. They were, more than likely, involved in the 'smithy' trade when they arrived in Ireland on invading Norman sailing-ships from northern France sometime in the fourteenth or fifteenth century.

It is said that every Curtis family had at least one Blacksmith in the clan. It would seem that with this ancient trade traditionally came a more arcane knowledge – the gift of 'Healing'. In one branch of the family this 'Gift' found expression in offering cures – often life-saving – to many human ailments. In our branch of the family it found expression in the curing of animals – especially horses.

In his travels around Clare in the late nineteenth century, the celebrated historian and author TJ Westrop, became aware of the family's 'Cure' (also called 'The Charm').

Westrop wrote:

"I am told that a Curtis of Kilnaboy, near Corofin, cures liver complaints, bleeding and cows that have swallowed potatoes. He puts his human patients on their backs on his anvil and pretends

to strike them with his sledge hammer. The patient then drinks
forge water. All the family have the gift of healing. A legend says
that St. Patrick's Horse lost a shoe near Kilnaboy and their ances-
tor shod it gratuitously. The saint therefore endowed the family
with the Power and people even return from America to be cured
by the smith."

('Folklore of Clare'. T.J. Westrop. Orig. publ. 1910-13.
Reprinted Clasp 2000)

My grandfather was the local Blacksmith when the historian
travelled here. Perhaps Westrop, like so many strangers and
travellers in those days, may have had his horse shod in the forge
before continuing on his way. My father Pat Joe (who along with
a younger sister, survived a TB plague which took three older
brothers, a sister and his mother to their graves between 1918
and 1920) was seventeen years of age and preparing to immi-
grate to the USA. Following the loss of almost the entire family
in less than two years he decided to stay and follow in his father's
footsteps. This meant farming the land and learning the
Blacksmith trade – as his father did before him – and taking on
the responsibility of 'The Cure'. This he did, excelling in and
practicing both disciplines until his death in 1980.

Though I had cautiously explored the Forge when my father
was out in the fields tending the farm, I was probably five or so
before I was considered grown enough to actually enter while
work was being done there. The Forge itself – a long, low,
thatched, stone-walled building with cobble-stone floor -was built
sometime in the late 1700's in the time of my Great-Grandfather
Patrick, who was born in 1775. One of the most valued heirlooms
to still survive from that time were a number of Pike (spear)-
heads hammered out by my ancestors in that same Forge in
preparation for the 1798 Rebellion.

For a small boy the attractions of the Forge were many. To the
left of the space where the horse would be tethered was the anvil
– bronze and shined from years of constant usage – seated on a
solid block of ancient black oak; very possibly an already aged,
living tree when Queen Elizabeth the 1st was still a girl. To the
right of the anvil, set underneath the rows of old horseshoes of
different shapes and hand-made forge pincers, punches and
rasps, was the Forge's centre Alter, the raised stone fireplace and
chimneystack. Adjacent to the fire was the water-trough, hewn

from solid limestone. (Another stone-trough sat outside the forge door; where, on hot summer days, horses would slake their thirsts while waiting their turns within.) It was said that there was a Cure for warts in the water of this trough and some, considering it a source of iron, drank from it.

But the primary focus of my childish attention was the huge bellows hidden in the deep shadows behind the fire and chimneystack. This massive wood and leather contraption fascinated me as I watched it heave and groan and breath life, like some mythical dragon, to the glowing coal fire into which my father plunged all manners, shapes and lengths of metals.

My first 'official' job in the forge was as 'Bellows Boy'. I was charged with a single task; I was to keep the coal-fire glowing red-hot by pulling the long, creaking timber arm which activated the massive old bellows (itself suspended on a sturdy wooden framework) into wheezing life. This I did, with as much energy and enthusiasm as my 5-year old body could produce, while watching and listening to the mysterious activities going on around me.

From first light and early cockcrow the farmyard bustled with life. Cows had to be milked and foddered, cow-cabins cleaned and fresh straw shaken on floors. Cattle had to be foddered in the fields and pigs, hens, geese, ducks and bronze turkeys and their chattering broods had to be fed and counted; an nocturnal visit from the neighbourhood fox or Pine Marten could cause havoc in the hen-house. These chores were all done to a cacophony of mooing, bleating, chirping, clucking, quacking: all in rhythm with the clanging of milk-buckets and creamery cans, feeding-pails and tins, barking dogs and squawking crows and magpies.

When winter days fell like a magic spell on the Burren and life and time itself slowed to a crawl, the Forge, and my father, rarely saw an idle moment. At first light the first horse and its owner, eager to be ahead of what would later build into a queue of as many as 6 or 7 horses, had already arrived in the yard and tying his horse to the still-closed forge-door. Pat Joe, his sleeves rolled up in preparation for a long days sweaty toil, stirred lazy fire-coals into life. As other farmers arrived with their horses, (some harnessed to carts or traps, some saddled and some on tow behind their walking owners) the men gathered inside the forge close to the glow and warmth of the now-raging coal-fire. Soon

the sound of loud conversation, along with that of groaning bellows, hammer on anvil and snorting horse, filled the Forge and
farmyard.

I recall the Forge in those days to be a hotbed of activity and
of animated and lively conversation, much of it beyond the understanding of a small boy. In these pre-radio or TV days, the Forge
offered the men-folk of the locality a safe, convivial and neutral
space to air opinions and views and to hear and discuss the latest news.

Topics discussed ranged from politics – local and national – to
cattle and pig prices at local fairs, potato, wheat and hay crops,
(how long it might take to get the hay saved and safely home,
because of the inclement weather, was a common topic) to stories
of strange or quirky goings-ons in the locality. There was news
and gossip from town and city and from far-away lands; often
supplied by the farmers' close relations now living and working in
England, in America or in far-off Australia.

Indeed, for many farmers – some married, some bachelors, iso-
lated, lonely and remote for six days of the week – this time spent
at the forge in company of my father and other farmers would be
greatly valued as a place of vital social contact and of high entertainment. Here, amid the smoke, sparks, clatter and clang – as
the Smithy plied his trade – they might renew old friendships,
heal fractured relationships and find some solace among their
peers.

While the men lit their pipes, filled with strong tobacco cut and
rolled from dark, thick plugs, and maneuvered to get close and
settle in by the fire (sometimes for the entire day), my father
rolled his sleeves up, donned his leather 'smithy' apron and set
about the job in hand; that of shoeing the waiting horse.

Should the horse require a set of 'removes', the job was rela-
tively straightforward. The old horseshoe was levered off the hoof
by pincer and, while the hoof was being scraped and pared with
a bone-handled hoof-knife, a new horseshoe reddened deep in the
core of the red-hot fire. While still glowing it was placed on the
anvil to be hammered into shape to refit the newly trimmed hoof.
A fitting would follow; the still-red shoe being placed on the hoof
that, (amidst a thick white cloud of acrid hoof-smoke) burned a
groove into which it would settle when finally fitted.

When Pat Joe was satisfied that the shoe was a comfortable fit, (after reheating and some final hammered curving and tapering) he plunged it into the water-trough to cool before placing it on the hoof and deftly hammering home the nails, clinching and finally rasping and trimming any overhanging hoof.

Making a 'new set' of shoes followed the same actions – except that the new shoe was cut from long lengths of grooved iron-bars and hammered into shape on the gleaming anvil.

When at last the long day was over and the satisfied farmers and their horses had departed, my father hung up his smithy apron, washed his hands and came indoors for a well-earned supper.

Work in the Forge was hard, sweaty and backbreaking. (Work that ultimately took its toll on my father's health.) But he continued to ply his ancient trade with pride and stamina until the horse more of less disappeared from the landscape. By the late 1960's and early '70's the horse as a working animal had almost been entirely replaced by the tractor and the motor-car and there was less and less call for the services of the traditional Blacksmith.

On those rare days when no horses waited to be shod, there was always other pressing 'smithy' work to be done in the forge. Cart wheels had to mended or shod and a motley collection of plough-shares, horse-drawn mowing-machines, iron gates and other assorted farm-implements – shovels, forks, billhooks, axes and scythes – all awaited repair work; and all, naturally, 'urgently' required by their owners.

After two hundred years of activity the Forge now stands idle and silent. No more the anvil tolls its hammered bells; no more the ancient bellows breathes life to a star-hot fire, no more the smoke curls from burning hoof or from the tall chimney-stack and no more the Blacksmith bends to his labours. While no other authentic forges from that period have survived, this Forge has weathered the years and the changes. And so it now stands, the only surviving genuine Blacksmith's Forge in the county. There is no smithy to work it however; and though the love of horses remains in our blood and bones, neither I, nor any of my siblings, (life had other plans for us) took up the ancient family trade of Blacksmithing.

Time has wrought many changes since this solid limestone building – more a museum these days – hummed with vitality, life and creative energy. Now the old Forge stands, solid and silent; a signpost to, and a reminder of, a very different, yet not so distant, past.

Now, more than a quarter of a century since the Forge saw its last working day, I sometimes push open the rust-hinged double-doors and enter within as I did as a boy.

While old ghosts rise and swirl about me, I tug at the creaking bellows and imagine I see the fire leap into life and hear once again the music of hammer on anvil, the talk and laughter of men these many years in their graves and scent yet again the heady perfumed admixture of animal and human sweat, iron-oxide and burning hoof as the Blacksmith plies his ancient trade.

This is the ancient music of the Forge.
A symphony that remains
and still rings clear.
The anvil-song that lives on in the Forge of Memory.

The Hill at the Back of My House

I can see the whole world
stretch out to hazy horizon.
Villages, cities, empires,
lime-dashed cottage, minarets spiralling.
I can see patchwork fields
laced with silk-thread streams,
like some priceless Persian carpet
a million years in the working,
countless hands in the weaving.
I can see the white-thorn blossom
in a silent forest of stone.
I can see the seasons
and the first butterfly of Spring
from the hill at the back of my house.

I can see the whole world
reach up to shipwreck clouds,
crumbling ruins and war-weary towers;
the battle now is with rook and ivy.
I can see the ghosts
of endless, marching armies
pass a herdsman and his dog.
I can see the full moon sit on treetops
while chuckling stars applaud.
I can see an ancient burial-mound;
it holds the bones
of my forefathers.
I can see myself,
from the hill at the back of my house.

41

Remembering Mariah

"I shall remember while the light lives yet
and in the night time I shall not forget."
'Erotion' by A.C. Swinburne

WITH THE PASSAGE OF TIME, SO WE are told, some people come to resemble their pets. Others, after years of living together, begin to take on the characteristics of their partners. To me, as a young boy, old Mariah looked as if she had been carved out of the very stone which surrounded the cottage in which she lived for all of her ninety-six years – her visage slate-gray, weather-lined, ancient.

Sometimes, when, as a mischievous lad of six or seven, I would peek in through her doorway and catch her snoozing in her whitethorn armchair, Mariah looked as if she had been replaced in the chair by some life-size ancient carving etched from stone. Until, that is, she awoke and her bright, sloe-black eyes transformed her features utterly, melting even the craggy limestone, which seemed determined to claim her.

"I know these stones." I remember her say. "And these stones know me."

Today, half a century later, as I walk the Burren's stony places I sometimes catch a glimpse of her features where a darting spike of evening light strikes a protruding jag or weather-beaten stone or falls softly on a sliver of rain-swept limestone gryke or flagstone.

In those moments, I can't help but think but that perhaps the stone did claim Mariah after all.

Old Mariah lived close by our house in a sheltered, compact cottage. The cottage, built by her own people sometime in the early eighteen hundreds, was without electricity, running water or any modern convenience. She was also a namesake and blood relation to the paternal side of our family. We never unraveled exactly what that relationship was but it would appear she was my grandfather's first or second-cousin, She was, my mother never tired of telling us, the oldest, wisest and most feared woman in the whole of the Burren. Most local people were convinced she would make the century; but, shortly after my ninth birthday in 1953, she let go the thread of life – a thread she had clung to with a fierce tenacity – at the great age of ninety-six.

Mariah was an extraordinary woman, in both looks and spirit and she possessed a razor sharp mind right up to the day she died. Tall, straight-backed, gaunt, white hair piled high in a plait under a lace-rimmed black bonnet and usually dressed, whatever the season, in long, black, flowing clothes over high-laced boots – in style when Queen Victoria was a girl – Mariah looked as if she had stepped directly out of the pages of a Dickens of a Jane Austin novel. If indeed, such had been the case, she would not have seemed half so exciting, mysterious or exotic to me as a young lad.

I remember her now, regally seated in her high-backed chair beside her open turf fire, speaking to me of her long life; her tales drawn from a river of clear memories flowing through nine decades of living in this very house. I recall her gentle smile each time I stepped into her kitchen. I recall the way her delicate, blue-veined, restless hands twitched and moved incessantly as she brushed away imaginary dust from her apron. I recall the way her slender fingers moved as if counting beads or danced on the grip of her walking stick while probing the stone floor at her feet; as one would test thin ice before stepping on it.

Mariah lived, and died, a spinster, the last of one branch of a family of renowned Healers. For several generations, people had flocked from far and wide to their cottage at the southern edge of the Burren, where she lived with her bachelor brothers Denis and Thomas (also called 'Robin'), to avail of their power to cure all manners of physical – and often psychological, complaints. Where regular doctors or apothecary's remedies had often failed, Mariah and her family could bring about cures that were deemed almost miraculous.

Though this gift of natural healing brought relief to all who sought it, Mariah's family endured an uneasy relationship with the local Clergy; who perceived their extraordinary healing powers as coming directly from Satan himself. And so it was Mariah and her siblings were demonized to the point of persecution because of these healing gifts and insights into the physical and spiritual human condition.

More than once my mother whispered to us youngsters,

"Mariah has the Power! Had she lived a few hundred years ago, they would have burned her as a witch!"

Witch!

The word conjured up frightful images of mediaeval terror. Images of a toothless, wizened old hag with broom and black cat, who would turn us children into sticks or stones or black crows to wander the Burren skies should we ever cross her, filled our over-active imaginations. Until we later learned that old Mariah was nothing like the sinister witches as portrayed in the picture-books, we gave her cottage a wide berth and ran in fear should she spot us in the vicinity and look on us with disfavour.

We were not the only ones who feared Mariah and her strange powers.

Partly in awe, partly in genuine fear of her strange unearthly gifts and powers, coupled with an air of mystery and danger, the more superstitious women of the locality would sometimes cover their faces with their shawls and scarves or turn their eyes away should they happen to encounter Mariah on the road.

The men too were uncomfortable in her presence and often gave her a wide berth. Was this, I often wondered, the reason she had lived her entire life a Spinster? How many young men had balked at the thought of approaching such a woman when she was still in her youth and prime with thoughts of courtship?

Very few, it would seem, given her reputation – and the reputation of her immediate family – in the locality.

The priests too felt uneasy at what they believed to be fact. And that was that Mariah possessed the 'Evil Eye' and should she cast that Eye – with intent – on any living person, that person was cursed with bad Luck – or worse, in danger of losing their very souls. They said as much from the pulpit and continually warned the people of the dangers and the evils of resorting to such people in their hour of need. Patently, such unexplained 'powers', the clergy reasoned, did not – could not – in their view, spring from Heavenly Sources.

Mariah's brother Brian had fared no better in his dealings with the local clergy. So far-reaching was his reputation as a Healer, that he earned for himself the Catholic Church's ultimate penalty – Excommunication.

The local clergy – often unenlightened, simple men – were most fearful and suspicious of any extraordinary human ability, which they could neither understand nor control. The Bishop, through the priests, sought to purge the flock of any such covert activities – and there were many – which smacked of the old pre-Christian, Pagan ways. The Hierarchy believed – with good reason – that beneath the veneer of the Christian Roman Catholic values as introduced by St. Patrick and his followers the local people harboured yet a deep and unspoken belief in the rituals and symbols of old Pagan Ireland. A great many local pagan superstitions abounded and there were, the clergy knew, too many local people who – even still – regarded Mariah and her brothers as being the 'unofficial' Priests and Priestesses of the 'Old Religion'. It was a heresy that had to be stamped out.

And so, sometime in the late eighteen nineties, Brian, because of his many witnessed and proven successes as a Healer, was identified above the others as suspect of being in league with the 'dark forces' was finally called to account. He was asked to admit and recant his attachment to the 'Black Arts', such as he and his family practiced, and to cease casting his 'Black Spells' on innocent, God-fearing people.

When he did not, (indeed he publicly scoffed at any and all such implications that his 'cures' came from the Devil) the clergy retaliated and Brian was banished from the flock – cast out into the Pagan darkness of Excommunication.

Brian's expulsion from the Catholic Church did not, by all accounts, halt the number of people who came seeking his (or Mariah's) aid as a Healer. The proof of the pudding, after all, was in the eating of it. When, in other safer times, the sick and troubled came in the light of day, now they came under the full cover of darkness. In the courtyard and out-houses outside the cottage, lanterns were seen to burn and shadowy figures often seen silently moving about into the wee small hours.

Following Brian's expulsion from the Catholic fold, (he was readmitted shortly before his death) no one in Mariah's household had much time for priests; though they continued to fulfill their duties as Catholics well enough.

Mariah fascinated me as a small boy and I visited her every chance I got. Initially I was scared to approach the house. She was after all, a 'Witch' who could, if displeased, upset or crossed, in any way, cast the most horrible of spells. Her stark and imposing appearance only seemed to confirm my worst fears and so my first visits to her house were no more than speedy and furtive glances over her half-door, before scurrying away tingling with fear and delight, her laughter ringing in my ears. When I finally drummed enough courage to venture beyond the door to her dark kitchen, I found myself in the company of a severe-looking – though truly gentle – wise old lady.

It was the beginning of a long series of visits and, before long; it became almost a daily event. I had, at last, found an adult who was prepared to talk to me for long periods during the long, hot summer days and in the warmth and glow of her open peat-turf fire in winter days. A picture of that small boy chattering away to that graceful old lady is forever frozen in my mind's eye.

Sometimes, when evening shadows lengthened outside her cottage door and when the talk died and Mariah nodded off, I would quietly sit and peer in to her open turf or wood fire or at the array of dark-blue, ruby or green bottles which lined her window-sills and dresser.

These old bottles, so my father told me, contained all manners of rare liquids – powerful herbal mixtures, secret cures, and magic potions. How mysterious! and how I longed to select, uncork and sip from any one of those mysterious bottles. But I well knew, that even as Mariah dozed, her 'Inner Eye' watched my every move and so I stayed my hand. I also well knew that one sip from the wrong bottle might change me forever into a hare or rabbit. and then where would I be!

It was said that she once changed somebody who had crossed her, into the biggest hare ever seen in the Burren and they were never seen in mortal form again.

Though I now felt at home and comfortable in her presence, I figured it best not to take any chances. If I truly felt courageous, as she dozed in her chair, I might tiptoe to her parlour door to steal a glance into the mysterious, permanent gloom – and wonder. The parlour also served as Mariah's bedroom and I gazed in amazement; marvelling at the imposing bulk of a massive four-poster bed, curtained in tasselled velvet drapes that dominated the room. On her bedside table sat an old faded photograph mounted in a silver frame; a tall coloured bottle in which stood a single peacock's feather and a huge leather-bound, metal-clasped family Bible. At the foot of the four-poster, stood a huge leather-bound sea-chest. Here, I was convinced, were hidden fabulous treasures beyond my wildest imaginings; gold sovereigns, foreign coins, glittering jewelled clasps, ruby-studded pendants, delicately-carved ivory figurines, sandalwood scented boxes and hand-mirrors, fabulous clothes of Chinese silks and satins, perhaps? How many time did Mariah tell me of these things.

She related how, in her younger days, she had attended the great 'soirees', balls and dances in the 'big houses of the rich and influential in Ennis and even further away, in Limerick city. To these affairs, Mariah – as she told it – wore such finery that would put the Queen of Sheba to shame.

There was, I was also convinced, another – more mysterious – treasure which lay in the chest. Here hidden, I imagined, was her famous silver-tipped hammer; which she – and her brothers – used to beat out a rhythm on a small anvil to the Healing mantras she recited when weaving one of her many Cures. Many believed that it was a magic hammer and that alone was the true source of her healing power. Mariah would say little except that she had received the hammer eighty or so years before from a strange travelling woman who arrived in the farmyard with her child one black January day. They were both starving and at death's door. Mariah, who was then ten years old, could see that the ragged skeleton and her baby were beyond human help and could do no more than direct the pitiful couple to an outhouse where they could find shelter from the cold night. She returned later with some broth, homemade bread and a jug of buttermilk. The woman thanked Mariah for her kindness and before she left them both for the night, the woman drew something from inside her ragged shawl and pressed it into Mariah's hand. In the glow of the lantern, a silver-tipped hammer glinted hard and sharp in the palm of her hand.

"I'm not long for this world . . . neither is the *leanbh*. This is my parting gift. It has the Power . . . use it only for good and never let it out of your hands . . . never!"

When Mariah and her father went to the stable the following morning they found two corpses -two more victims of the great famine, still sweeping through the land and claiming souls.

Almost a century on from that day, she still possessed the hammer, so she said, safe and hidden and maybe someday soon she would meet that travelling woman and return her gift to her.

It made perfect sense to me that Mariah would secret the hammer among her most valued possessions in the old wooden chest. How I longed to see inside that old chest! My heart would beat faster at the very thought of it. Perhaps here, I imagined, along with her life's most treasured belongings and keepsakes, might lie her rarely seen book of ancient cures and spells. Knowing her remaining days were few, Mariah had once offered this book to my father (he being her only living close blood-relative) and which he refused in the belief that he did not deserve access to such arcane knowledge.

"I'll burn the book." Mariah had said after my father refused to accept her offer. "I'll burn it rather than let that book fall into the hands of fools or those with no right to possess it!"

And so I desperately longed that one day Mariah would invite me inside her parlour and reveal the contents of that carved chest. She never did however. After her death and the arrival of new occupants in the house, the four-poster bed, the Book of Cures, the cigar-box containing her uncle's war-medals, her silver tipped hammer and anvil, – the sea-chest with all its secrets intact – all mysteriously disappeared never to be seen again.

"Aren't you the great young fella to be visiting old Mariah." She would greet me, always referring to herself in the third person. "We'll have a drop of something to warm us."

She said this whatever the weather, whatever the season and I always nodded my agreement. In any case no one – young or old – argued with Mariah; and I wasn't about to set a precedent.

I had, over my frequent visitations, developed an inordinate liking for her excellent home-brewed beverages. These included extremely potent sloe, elderberry and rose-hip wines and I was treated to each when they had matured enough to be sampled. I never dared mention any of this at home, but my mother must have often wondered way, after a prolonged visit with Mariah, I would sometimes sneak to my bedroom for long naps.

Once I had stepped inside and was seated by the hearth, Mariah would rise and shuffle off into her permanently darkened parlour and after much talking to herself, she would emerge with two bottles, a tall-stemmed wine glass, a tin mug and an old cake-tin adorned with a kilted, bearded Scots Bagpiper. From the murkier of the two bottles, she would pour me a glass of sloe or elderberry wine and hand it to me with a plateful of musty-smelling, broken biscuits from the cake-tin. From the other bottle, which I later learned to be a brandy-bottle, she would pour a liberal helping into her rose-embossed tin mug. I also later learned that Mariah was extremely partial to that particular bottle.

"That woman would be pushing up daisies years ago . . . if it wasn't for the Hennessy family. That's what's keeping her alive . . . the brandy . . . and the oysters!" My father often remarked. It was true that Mariah also had a marked passion for best fresh oysters, which she had regularly delivered to her door from Liscannor and there was always a pile of open shells outside her front door. The empty brandy bottles she kept well out of sight.

Hardly a day, summer or winter, went by without me visiting Mariah and her bad-tempered dog, Charlie. In the course of those many visits, I grew to love her as I would a favourite aunt. I loved her for the fact that she talked to me as an adult. I loved her reminiscing aloud. I marvelled at her stories and tall tales of ancient Irish warriors and their fierce battles, feasts and romances. I thrilled at her descriptions of the long-dead Gaelic heroes and De Danann giants who once walked this land and raised the great stone-forts and mysterious stone-dolmens which now dotted the stony landscape all about us. And I loved the way my skin would creep when she whispered of the myriad troubled spirits and restless ghosts which stalked the lanes and byways.

From Mariah I learned of the headless horseman who nightly galloped the highways but could never cross over a river, stream or any running water.

I sat in breathless silence as Mariah told me of the faceless, black-cloaked driver aboard the 'Coiste Bower' – the ghost funeral coach pulled by four plumed black horses and whose appearance always foretold the death of a neighbour; as did the nocturnal wailing of the Banshee by the well.

She had, she told me, seen with her own eyes the Death Coach come rumbling down the road from the nearby graveyard and she had often seen the Banshee and the old Fairy Woman of the Road as She sheltered from wind and rain at the midnight hour beneath a nearby haunted Hawthorn. A death always followed such ghostly sightings.

In the fading light of an early winter evening and while November winds moaned its lonesome song outside her cottage door, Mariah whispered to me of the shadowy inhabitants of the Otherworld; whom she swore she could see and with whom she conversed on a regular basis. Sometimes she would recite – mantra-like and low – the names of the long-dead (the famine dead, so my father said) and the names of local people who had died long before Mariah was born. On the days around All Souls Day these restless spirits of the long-dead visited and remained with Mariah for short periods.

"They're here with us now!" She would sometimes whisper – especially when long evening shadows came down upon us and she had supped heartily from her tin cup. "Don't you see them? Look! up there . . . in the rafters!"

She pointed her leather-thonged walking stick toward the arched and darkened smoke-stained ceiling. I looked up and . . . yes! . . . I too could see them. First as shadows, hushed and still high among the rafters and then, as if being shaped out of thin air by her very words, they slowly took nebulous shape to silently sit in observance of us – the living – seated underneath.

I was more than glad to escape Mariah's company following such sightings and usually covered the short distance between her front door and home – my skin tingling and crawling with excitement and fear – in double-quick time.

I hardly ever saw Mariah outside the house. Once, in late September, I saw her picking Sloe berries from a laden bush in the laneway leading from her cottage. And I well remember one dew-wet morning in late Spring, while gathering in cows from the pastures for early milking, I caught sight of her, talking to herself while prodding and poking the earth with her stick in the field behind her cottage. I thought to hail her, but did not as she seemed utterly engrossed in whatever it was in the hedgerow, which held her full attention.

"Gathering wild herbs, mushrooms and roots to concoct one of her potions or Cures, no doubt." My mother whispered (she

51

always whispered whenever she spoke of Mariah as if relating
some dark or dangerous secret), when I told her of my early-
morning sighting.

For me, as a boy not yet ten years old, each visit to Mariah was
special. Each one charged with the electricity of excitement and
of wondrous boyish expectation. To step inside her cottage door
and to sit across the hearth from her and listen to her speak, was
to enter into a world infused with an atmosphere of mystery and
magic. A world she brought to life with vivid colour, vision and
vitality. It was from these threads that Mariah spun and weaved
her stories from her extraordinary web of memory and words.
Her sharp intellect, her almost total recall from a lifetime's store
of memories and experiences, her powers of articulation and
descriptive speech, her perceptions and insights into the human
condition; her unique vision and creative spirit; her sense of place
in a world of strongly-observed traditions and social behaviour;
her personal struggles, failures and successes in that world, her
loves and losses, memories and opinions, were all part of this
extraordinary old woman.

But above all, even as she knowingly faced her last few weeks
on this earth, she still radiated an undimmed hunger for, and
love of, life. This Mariah expressed in her ability to live fully in
the gift of each living moment, her fearless acceptance of things
as they are and perhaps, most of all, her willingness to talk with
both patience and frank openness to a young boy; only half-
understanding the wondrous gifts she was offering and he,
unknowingly, was receiving.

Somebody once said that only our memories allow that some
people ever existed; that their lives, their thoughts, their actions
mattered. I hardly know another living soul alive today who
remembers Mariah as I do. I think of her often these days. I
remember so much about her; her inner strength of spirit; her
sheer indominatable will to live, to accept, experience and treasure each day as it came. Most of all I remember her stories,
strange and wonderful, magical and surreal, told as if unfolding
-chapter by chapter – the book of her long, eventful life to a small
boy who, enthralled, sat and listened to a special old woman; the
likes of whom, I know in my deep heart, I will never again meet
in my life.

A Burren Christmas

HAVING JOURNEYED THROUGH AND survived, as best we might, all the past twelve months could hurl at us, we finally approach once again that special time of the year that is like no other – Christmas. For some, it is but yet another poisoned pool in a desert of darkness, a time of pain, sadness, hopelessness and loneliness.

For most of us, hopefully, it offers an Oasis of Light, Hope and Happiness in an increasingly troubled and turbulent world. A time of physical and spiritual; a gentle time renewal of inner peace and gentle reflection.

Each of us approaches Christmas in our own way; each one carrying within our hearts the reverberations – good and bad – of Christmas' past and the dreams and hopes of Christmas' to come.

In cities and towns there is a quickening in pace, as shops and stores prepare to cope with increased seasonal business. Television and radio urge sorely-pressed shoppers to part with hard-earned money while street Christmas-lights, often switched on since early November, glimmer with a cold, commercial glow and serve to further beckon and entice us to spend.

However, Christmas in the country is quite different. Here in the Burren, it is serene, beautiful and strangely mysterious. The gray mantle of winter has long since been cast over the land and in this silent world of stone, the pale, low-lying sun, when it peeps through, highlights a rich tapestry of deep-winter colours. There are carpets of furze, hazel-bush and of bracken, in every possible hue of russet and dark-brown. So too are the varied mosses, and other winter shrubs.

The trees of Christmas, the Rowan and Ivy, are in their full

55

regalia of blossom. You will experience no green so startling as that of a lone holly-bush pushing up from a craggy limestone fissure. Startling too is the sight of red holly-berries on a bush which was previously barren. Peer a little closer and you may be rewarded with a glimpse of a tiny robin perched among the prickly holly-leaves glistening with silver droplets of rain; its red breast competing madly with a profusion of berries. Green, red and silver – the colours of a Burren Christmas. For a moment it might seem as if you have stepped into a giant living Christmas card. The turloughs, dry throughout the summer and now gorged since the October rains, teem with winter bird-life – Greenland duck, widgeon, teal, shoveller, heron and wild swan. A Christmas sky can be transformed by the sight, and wondrous music, of a V-formation flight of swans winging towards the horizon and that safe nesting place on some nearby body of sheltered water. This year's floods have brought hundreds of swans to add grace and quiet, frosty beauty to the Burren turloughs, ponds and lakes. Can you picture anything so peaceful, so calming, so exquisitely serene as catching a glimpse of these most beautiful of Nature's shapes, gliding as softly as falling snowflakes on a liquid mirror? (A Zen moment – which remains with one long after the sighting).

On the slopes of another of Nature's most extraordinary designs, Mullaghmore – the beating heart of the Burren – a King Billy-goat glares down from his rocky throne before tossing his wild, shaggy head and disdainfully leading his harem to even higher, safer ground. Venture closer to the base of the hill and marvel at the profusion of timid plant-life sheltering deep in limestone grykes. Or at the array of fossilised shell and quartz-stone, glittering gems, strewn by some extravagant Creator's hand, glistening in shafts of winter sunlight among the flagstone. Flapping heron's wings beat ripple-waves in both the still-air twilight and turlough surface alike. Winters here, for both animals and man, are mild. It's not unusual for Christmas Day temperatures to sometimes equal that of a Mid-summer day. Only occasionally are the turloughs, lake's and rivers encrusted in icy casings: which, when the east wind flutters and moves across frozen, sculpted surfaces, zing and sing like a thousand plucked harp-strings; resonating deep in the heart's core long after the ice has melted.

Though children may dream of snowflakes on Christmas Day, white Christmases in the Burren are extremely rare. The oldest locals can only recall a Christmas Day snowfall on one or two occasions. But children, big and small, can dream. Who can tell, perhaps this year, dreams may turn to falling Christmas snowflakes. When the silence of early darkness falls on the stone, it is a silence you can hear; broken only by the cry of a night-bird, the lowing of distant cattle or the bleating of a lost sheep.

Watch out for the night prowlers and hunters when you drive through the quiet country roads – the fox, stoat, pine-marten and badger. The nighttime is their time, and you are within their Kingdom. In the east a star twinkles brighter than the rest. Under such a star you might expect to catch sight of three camels and their Kingly riders silhouetted against the night sky.

What matter that the star is the planet Mars, God of War – inexorably moving closer to the earth. While some men make wars, such stars set other men's imagination alight. To stand and to listen for a moment between the stone and dropping sky is to hear the sound of the Burren asleep. A sleeping limestone world of whitewashed cottage, of great stone-dolmens, stone-forts, stone-castles and dry-stone walls, deep in winter slumber. You can sense though that nature is not asleep, but awaiting a signal. Awaiting, perhaps, the fierce flame of a Solstice Ritual fire or the soft warm glow of a single candle alight in a window. All awaiting the Bells of Christmas to ring out their eternal message of rebirth and of renewal, the age-old signal to awaken. In this moment of deepest winter darkness, this moment of ancient magic, summer is conceived.

Indoors, around the warmth of the home-heart, other images conspire to weave that special magic that comes only at Christmas. The warmth of a turf fire piled high, the crackle and spit of flaming beech, chestnut or ash logs, the soft glow of a oil-lamp, the scent of apple, of cinnamon and of cloves and other spices, the sharpness of the winter night air and the strange stillness which descends after midnight. These images can turn the mind to nostalgic reflection and memories of time gone by. In this quiet time, I recall past Christmases and the flurry of activity in our house (the house I now inhabit) that always preceded Christmas.

My mother ran a small country shop at the southern edge of the Burren. This was in the days before Supermarkets, Megastores and Shopping Malls and local people shopped locally; which meant a busy time for our little shop. In the two weeks coming up to Christmas Eve there were many chores for us youngsters to do in the recently seasonally decorated shop – tea, sugar and plain white flour (which all came in bulk) had to be weighed in 1 lb and 2 lb bags. So too did the Christmas Cake and Plum- Pudding ingredients – almonds, raisins, currants and sultanas, stick lemon- peel, and suet had to be chopped and weighed; so did the various nuts and exotic spices – ginger, cinnamon, cloves, nutmeg. Lists of Christmas provisions – always lengthy and detailed – dropped in to the shop earlier, had to be selected and packed in canvas bags, baskets or cardboard boxes. Added to the usual regular provisions were the special Christmas luxuries – Red jellies and jams, custards, tinned peaches or pears, oranges (a rare exotic fruit in those days), loose biscuits, bottles of blood-red cordial, dark chocolates and sticky can-sweets. This hamper would be topped off with a dark fruitcake for the family or a wedge or two of Plug tobacco for the man of the house and two or three giant red Christmas candles. As a token and a seasonal gesture, a special Christmas Box, (a present for regular customers) was then added by my mother, who distributed these gifts according to the size of the customer's annual spending.

Suddenly Christmas Eve is upon us and holly, ivy and laurel boughs (a tradition which predates any Christian ritual) had to be gathered for house decorations. There never was a tradition of putting up a Christmas tree in our house in those days. Indeed such was the case in most country houses around. The putting up of the now-common Christmas tree is a tradition that has come into being only since the coming of television in the sixties. There always was a Nativity crib however; a simple wooden structure that was built, thatched, placed on a special plinth and decorated by my father with silver paper and freshly gathered laurel boughs and ivy strips.

For my mother, Christmas Eve was one of the busiest days of the year. The shop was busy from morning till night; the goose or turkey had to be plucked and stuffed; jellies, trifles and other savouries had to be made and her home-made Christmas cake had to be iced and decorated.

For us youngsters, high excitement reigned all through the day, increasing in intensity as early darkness fell on the land.

At five o'clock we gathered around the radio to listen in awe as Santa Claus read the names of those lucky few to be picked from his mail-sack before setting off on his long, nocturnal, global journey. At six o'clock sharp, a giant red Christmas candle was lit and placed in the kitchen window, usually by the youngest member of the family and the other candles were lit from it before being placed in every window throughout the house-upstairs and down. My father would then fill, raise and drink a glass of Whiskey in remembrance of those departed souls: who once lived in this house and celebrated bygone Christmas Eves; as we now did. Then we would go outside to look at the great display of candles alight in the windows of both ours and of neighbouring houses.

What a magical, transformed landscape spread out before our eyes! To me it seemed as if a shower of stars had fallen to earth and which now lay twinkling all around as far as the eye could see. The moment we had longed for all year had arrived; the moment of wonder and of magic and we had entered a Fairyland of light and love that only fully existed at Christmas-time. Back indoors, fires were placed and lit in every fireplace, light flickers and falls on holly-bough and coloured decorations and reflects on silver-edged Christmas cards with a holy light. My mother – finished with last-minute chores – would at last take her old fiddle from its case, rosin the bow and play her favourite reels and jigs and my father would recall tales of Christmases long ago, sing a snatch of a song or poem and end with a ghost story or two to add to the joy and happiness of an already highly-charged Christmas Eve atmosphere.

At last, with imaginations aflame and delirious with expectant excitement, it is time for bed and sweet dreams of what Santa Claus and the morning would bring; and we never were disappointed. Books, train-sets, and games – we always got more than we ever truly expected.

Just before drifting to fitful, happy sleep under a warm quilt, I would gaze through the frosted window-pane to witness the stars sparkling brighter than they had done on any other night of the year and I would strain to hear some distant sound.

There always was a sound, faraway but definite. It was the sound heard by boys and girls, men and women since the dawn of creation; it was the sound of the Winter Solstice, the sound of Hanukkah, the sound of Christmas – the sound of bells, gently tinkling. Now, no longer a child, I still listen for those Christmas bells – though perhaps they ring a little more distant than when I was a boy – before sleep comes on a peaceful Christmas Eve.

Part II

Stone Mountain
Poems

The Stone Mountain

Primal Landscape
Pagan Place.
Rainswept silver stone, mysterious Turloughs.
Unseen bird-cries, wings flocking,
Kestrel, Coot and Perigrine Falcon,
Raven, Rook and Tufted Duck.
Lakewater lapping, colours raging,
Cat's Feet, Dog Rose, Bloody Cranesbill,
Cowslip, Butterworth and Devil's Scabious.
Glistening dawn mists,
cloud-dark hillface,
sky and evening endless falling.
Keeper of Time, Keeper of No-time.
Home of Echo, Pan and Earth Mother Gaia.

Call out to the Land and the Land calls back.
Mullaghmore, *An Mullagh Mór*.
Velvet soft, Diamond hard.
Ageless Sacred Mountain.

The Speaking Stones

Here is where,
once,
the Gods themselves
did mighty battle,
raising a fortress
no mortal might imagine.
Ravaged by troubled skies
and gnawing, grasping oceans.
Now,
only the rocks remain.

Here is where,
once,
fearsome Lon MacLiofa
rang tunes of anvil-fire
on bleak Glas Gaibneach hill
and Danann's wizards
swept down magic mists
on this corner of Destiny's Isle.
Now,
only the rocks remain.

Here is where,
once,
the Seed of a nation
stood and – as battle's clamour
pierced the skies –
blooded gold,
(cast off by some dying Prince?)
lay in wait for another age.

Now,
only the rocks remain.

Here is where,
once,
the Mystics Colman and Cronan
communed with the Source
of all and gained *Satori*.
In the bittern's cry and rustling reeds
and by the tinkling streams
at the Eagle's Rock, lay eternity's vision,
Now,
only the rocks remain.

Here is where
once,
on lonely Sliabh Carran's slopes,
Donnchad, Prince of Thomond,
and his Clansmen
were haunted by dreams
and long-dead warriors
rose up and dolmens moaned.
Now,
only the rocks remain.

Here is where
once,
Maire Rua on her milk-white stallion rode
and spat in the eye of fate.
While inside her castle walls,
around brazen winter fires
and groaning festive tables,
she dreamed of a Crown but courted the worm.
Now,
only the rocks remain.

Here is where
now stalk history's ghosts.
The voiceless crying of nameless bones
murmer on April breezes
or shriek on bitter December winds.
How they cry out to us
from fort and cairn and tumulus,
to listen!
These silent stones speak loud
and low, of past, of future.

Burren Rocks

Like silicon sentinals they stand,
Guardians of the Hallowed Garden
of Time itself.
Silent and watchful
yawning at the edge of Creation.

Limestone warriors in legions strewn
like the dead on Elysian fields.
Shrouded with stardust
and the bones
of the men from the mists.

Watchers of ten million seasons;
perfumed by breezes laden
with the drones of the centuries.
The fossilised cry
of the ancients chronicled for ever.

Megalithic messages hewn
by the Immortals;
their secrets driven deep
into uncharted tombs
by the raging winds of Time.

Glittering in myriad frosted fonts,
the reflected glory of long dead stars
and crumbled empires.
While the centuries drop away
plashing on galactic window-panes.

Altars of flagstone retched
from a grumbling underworld.

Baptised in fire, purified in ice.
Unsullied yet by the bloodied boot
of Sultan or Caeser.

While mortals and their deeds,
like silken spectres,
glide across this stoney kingdom,
its frozen Kings and subjects hold back
the future from their Enchanted Court.

On the First Day of Spring

Robe the hills in pagan beauty,
Turquoise, violet, tumbled blues.
Splashed on mosses, arched at sunset,
Twilight afire with mysterious hues.

Goat bells jangling on a craggy slope,
Winter to his Dolmen fading,
April's purple conquerers looming,
Intense rossettes parading.

Flimsy butterfly, dreamlike, fluttering,
Spanish gold on drowsy wing.
While stones resound to Flutes of Pan
Piping in a new-born Spring.

Then paint the days with sound and colour
Nature's sap rising, surging
And blaze through the night the diamond stars
At birth of Spring from summer's yearning.

The Sound of Stone

Come a little closer
and feel the pulse
of this perfumed earth,
and the heartbeat
of these ancient stones.

Stand in the silence
and listen to the music
that floats
in the still air.
It is the sound
of the stones, singing.

Part III

The Music
of Ghosts

Nothing to Worry About

IN THE FADING LIGHT KATE BARELY NOTICED the grey, monotonous curtains of rain, which swept past her cottage window. It was now mid-November and a leaden sky melted its contents almost daily over the surrounding countryside. For a long time she gazed at rivulets of rainwater as they cut intricate designs on the kitchen windowpane, before turning away and moving slowly towards the fireplace. Stabbing a poker through the fire-grate at a fire struggling to come alive inside an ancient blackened range, Kate called out, "Mother, do you want a cup of . . ."

Her words trailed off to a whisper and she stopped her jabbing at the reluctant sparks. Kate still found it hard to accept. Her mother was dead. Dead and buried these seven . . . no, eight days now, and Kate would never again hear her mother's voice in this room . . . or see her sit in this room . . . in that chair . . . ever again.

With a deep sigh, Kate sat down slowly and gazed at the rugged old green-painted rocking chair by the fireside. Feeling a tear rise, she brushed a sleeve across her eye and continued to stare at the vacant chair. Suddenly she realised that, apart from the final days when her mother was too ill to leave her bed, she had never seen the chair quite so empty before. For as long as Kate could remember, this was her mother Molly's favourite chair. Now the old rocker – still draped with Molly's faded tartan shawl – seemed to her so desperately abandoned and forlorn; a fleshless, green, wooden skeleton alone and forsaken in the corner of the kitchen. The dying light fell for an instant on a spider

77

web in the making attached between one of the rocker skates and the nearby sidewall.

Kate blinked back a tear, then another and yet another. The clocked ticked a steady tattoo to her blinking and Kate began to cry. At first the tears came accompanied by slow, choking sobs; then came a tidal wave of tears utterly blinding her and her breast heaved as if some enormous, invisible weight pressed in on her ribcage squeezing her heart. The sobbing quickened in pace, registering finely as one, long, high-pitched wail.

Kate heard the cry as if coming from the throat of some trapped animal close by her in the room, yet knowing that it came from somewhere deep inside her. She suddenly became scared of the sound as it reverberated around the room. It was like none she had ever heard before, and though she tried to strangle it, still the strange, anguished cry that filled her ears and her head flowed unbidden out through every pore in her body. When the weight that gripped her heart like a falcon's talons seemed about to explode throughout her breast, the dis- embodied crying stopped. Now it was quiet again, with only her rapid heartbeat louder than the tick of the clock and the wind rapping and pushing at the windows and doors.

"They're gone." Kate murmured. 'They're both gone forever and there's nothing I do from this day on will bring them back."

She took a deep breath, shook herself to movement and reached for the kettle on the range-top. "I was going to make tea anyway." Kate said. Her hands, she noticed, were trembling and she reached instead for a packet of cigarettes lying on the table. Pulling one from the opened packet, she lit it and inhaled deeply.

"Jesus! I'm over fifty and this is the first time I've ever smoked in front of my . . ." Kate paused, glancing at the rocker, ". . . in the house."

She felt a pang of guilt as she sucked again at the cigarette, half expecting to hear her mother, who would not abide smoking in the house, protesting her actions.

The last year looking after Molly, in her final illness, had been a strain on both women. The old woman, though never overly quarrelsome, possessed a will of iron, an independent streak and a mind as sharp as a blade right to the very end.

"Am'nt I lucky to have you still with me Katie! I'd be in a home by now only for you . . . and I'd sooner drown myself in the lake than be packed away in one of them homes full of sick old folk. I want to die in my own bed . . . with my only daughter at my side. It's not too much to ask, is it?"

Molly said this often, especially whenever Kate was preparing to go out on a Sunday afternoon; the only day in the week she could claim as hers and hers alone to do with as she pleased. For the rest of the week she was a housebound nursemaid and companion to the dying Molly.

"Mother, you are old . . . and you are sick!" Kate would answer, as much to herself as to her mother.

The singing of the boiling kettle brought Kate back to the present, only to have another image crowd her mind. Now she recalled that Sunday, a year ago last Mayday, when she went out with James for the very last time. May was Kate's favourite month of the year. The light and air, the scents and sounds; they all seemed to conspire to create a landscape of energy, of hope and of life. The carpets of flowers and the intoxicating scent of the whitethorn was enough to make a person tipsy, she always thought.

It was on such a May day that Sunday that Kate slipped into her rose-patterned dress, her best low-heeled shoes and prepared herself to go out. James liked to see her in that dress; and anyway, it was her only good dress – her Sunday dress – other than her weekday working clothes. As she brushed her hair, she perused herself in the bedroom mirror.

"You're no beauty, Kate my girl." Kate said to the slim, tall figure staring back from the cracked sideboard mirror. "But your heart is in the right place."

Brushing an imaginary something from her sleeve, she added. "And sometimes I think it's the only thing that is!"

Kate smiled a slow smile. James liked her as she was – the way God made her – and he told her so often and anyway, she had long ago stopped envying other, younger, single woman their looks and their youth.

Kate had been seeing James Flynn for over six years now. Neither of them was in the first flush of youth, and though James had never actually broached the topic, Kate understood that a day would come when they would marry and settle down. There were, however, certain obstacles that barred them from achieving that goal – their respective mothers.

James Flynn was an only son who – like Kate – lived alone with Bessie, his aging, ailing mother in the neighbouring parish and she – like Kate's mother – also required constant care and attention.

Bessie Flynn had made it known to James from the time he reached manhood that there was going to be "no young 'missy'" – as she put it – move in and run the Flynn household. At least not as long as she lived; and she had every intention of reaching the century. And so James, and Kate – like so many others of their generation – were sentenced to bide their time and wait; for exactly what, neither one dared to speak aloud.

Kate once confided in an old and trusted school friend.

"There's nothing to worry about, Kate." Her friend Nancy consoled her. "Isn't James in the same boat as you are? Everyone knows his mother Bessie is one salty old bitch with an eye that would stop a grandfather clock, a tongue that would curdle buttermilk and a humour that would turn wine into water. The old bat can't live forever, now can she? Then he'll be free to start thinking about tying the knot. There's nothing to worry about Kate, It'll all work out in the end, you'll see."

Well, perhaps it would, Kate thought – but when?

Time was less on her side than on James', and Kate chilled at the thought that their future happiness depended on James's mother's death. Then there was the situation with Kate's own mother . . . she banished the dark thought from her mind and accepted the reality of her relationship with James Flynn.

Later, on her way to meet James at their usual meeting place some five miles from the house, Kate felt a growing unease; a gnawing premonition of something dark and shadowy about to invade her life and threaten her future happiness.

She breathed in the May aromas and tried to banish the shadow from her mind. She was not going to let anything spoil the few precious hours in the company of the man she hoped one day to marry. Though she tried to dispel it, a nagging sense of unease still lingered. James was not the most talkative of men at the best of times, but these last few Sundays, he seemed detached and preoccupied and had hardly uttered a dozen words to her during their hours together.

"Perhaps he'll out with it today . . . whatever it is that's bothering his head." Kate said into the fresh breeze as she leaned on the bicycle pedals and pushed on towards her Sunday rendezvous.

Usually Kate was the first to arrive but today James was

already waiting in his parked Morris Minor at their usual cross-roads meeting-place, roughly equi-distant from each other's houses. As she approached the parked car, the uneasy feeling she had experienced earlier again swept down on her mind.

"I didn't expect to find you here before me. You're early today." Kate greeted him as she dismounted and patted down her ruffled dress and hair.

"Am I? I didn't notice the time." James smiled as he greeted her in his usual shy, awkward way. Kate leaned her bicycle by a briar-adorned wall and slipped into the passenger seat beside him. They did not hug; they did not kiss; they did not touch.

"I'm usually the one who has to do the waiting." Kate laughed, "How are you James?"

"Oh! I'm fine . . . fine." He sounded distant.

Kate studied his face for a few moments.

"Right, James, out with it . . . what's the matter? You've been bothered by something or other these last few weeks? Are you in some sort or trouble?"

James sighed, "Trouble? No trouble . . . but there is one thing, Katie . . . Listen, I . . . I have to go into the Hospital on Tuesday . . . for some check-ups . . . routine tests . . . blood . . . x-rays . . . nothing too serious . . . I'll only be gone a few days . . . the neighbour Mrs. Carroll will look after the mother . . . there's nothing to worry about, so the doctors say."

He brightened as a slow, forced smile moved across his face, "And you know that they say, "There are only two things to worry about. Either you are well . . . or you are sick. If you are well, there's nothing to worry about." So I've nothing to worry about. I'm as right as rain"

His words tumbled out in single rush of breath. He looked straight ahead as he spoke, his smile fading and Kate could not help notice his knuckles whiten as he gripped the steering wheel.

"You've been to see a doctor? When? . . . You never mentioned it!" Kate tried to disguise the nervousness in her voice. He looked much paler, thinner than before; his cheeks seemed sunken his clothes now hung loosely on his once broad frame. Why had she not noticed this before? Maybe it was the fact that James Flynn, as she and everyone in both parishes knew, was as hardy and healthy as a horse and had never been in sick, or indeed in hospital, for a single day in his life.

Whatever it was that dogged him these last few months would

be sorted out for once and for all next Tuesday in the County Hospital.

There was no talk of illness or hospitals for the rest of their time together that afternoon. Later, as they parted, James, sensing her unease, drew her to him fiercely, kissed her, and just as fiercely drew back from her to hold her at arm's length.

"Don't worry, Katie love." Though his eyes blazed, his voice was gentle. "I'll see you next Sunday. I'll be fine. There's really nothing to worry about, nothing at all!"

Kate only saw James once again in the County Hospital Cancer Ward, a week before he died.

She could not bring herself to face the ordeal of his funeral. How could she face that? Who would be there who would understand? Who was there who could even begin to understand the raw grief that tore at her very flesh or her gut-wrenching sense of absolute loss?

The day they laid him in the grave, she went instead to their favourite spot by the river and sat for hours staring into the flowing waters that bore away her falling tears. Later, in her bed, Kate battled with the overwhelming shame at her failure at not flinging herself into the swollen floodwaters.

In the numb days that followed, life went on as normal. If her mother noticed her grim mood, she never inquired of Kate. In that way, daily life ticked by to the rhythm of time and tides; the waxing and waning of the moons and Saint's Days and Sundays.

Sundays were the worst, Kate took to locking herself in her bedroom to weep and struggle with her grief and loss till her whole body ached and spent she would fall into a half-conscious sleep. Later, there was a new pain to bear – that of regret, which seemed to overwhelm all the others.

When Molly died in the spring of the following year, Kate was shocked at just how calmly she reacted and conducted herself throughout her mother's wake and funeral. The pain she had suffered all those hollow days and cruel, empty nights had so wrung her dry of emotion and grief, she had little left to give her own mother at her passing.

Even Nancy commented later to her how calm and dignified she was and how well she had handled the whole affair.

Now, looking around the kitchen through tired, red-rimmed eyes, Kate noticed just how much larger everything seemed; the dresser, the cups and plates, the old brown table, the stuffed horse-hair sofa by the wall, Molly's old green rocker. It was as she remembered it as a small girl; yet it was like as if she was seeing the room and its contents for the very first time. She went to the cupboard where Molly kept her only two bottles of alcoholic drink – one bottle of Brandy and one of Port. Kate reached for the brandy bottle, uncorked it, and poured a large helping into a cup. She corked the bottle and replaced it back in the cupboard.

She moved slowly towards the rocking chair and stood for a long while staring down at it.

Finally she turned and eased herself down onto its seat. Turning her head, she laid her cheek against the plaid shawl draped over the chair-back.

"Still smells of mother." Kate thought. The chair was not uncomfortable; as she had imagined it might be. Slowly she pushed the rocker into creaking action and raised her cup to the fireplace in salute.

The sound of the gentle creaking of timber on stone filled the room. Outside the cottage, the rain had stopped and the moon showed its face as it peeked at the world through eastward-rushing rain-clouds.

"Good luck, Katie!" Kate said aloud, gently easing the chair back and forth. "Good luck. There's nothing to worry about, girl! Nothing at all to worry about."

St. Brigid's Day

At the first surge
of Spring,
January's dull and clinging ache
dies at last
and a single petal
melts the jagged edge
of winter's thorn.

Sacred dawn light
gracing hilltop,
stream
and patient stone.
Long night's darkness
banished
On this St. Brigid's Day.

The Music
of Ghosts

SOMETIMES, FROM WITHIN THE DEEP *swirling pool of dreams, comes a sound, which spins upwards, like a lark ascending. The sound is distant, high and lonesome. It is the sound of a fiddle and it comes without warning and always through the dark blood and thick-limbed shroud of troubled sleep.*

But with it there always comes an ease of recognition; a salve of beautiful melody to soothe a troubled spirit.

The tune the dreamer hears is always the same tune, the same half-forgotten melody; its lilt and rhythm spiralling through the formless shadow of dream-time like specks of dust dancing on a shaft of morning light.

Always from out of this silver mist of sound came a face. It is the face of a woman in her youth and prime; before the cares and troubles of the world etches its webbed map of life on her features. In the dream, the woman is young, smiling and happy. A fiddle is tucked beneath her chin.

Fingers flick and fall easily on vibrating strings. The fiddle-bow rises and dips as if dancing to the sound it is helping to shape.

The dreamer reaches out to attract the player's attention; to let her know he is close, that he is attentive to the music, which flows from her plaintive fiddle. But her eyes are shut tight to all but her music and her smile is only for the sad, old notes, which rise like tired ghosts from the singing strings.

Then, just before coming awake, the dreamer is filled with the bittersweet pain of loss; though laced with some deeper, unnamed grief. But he is filled too with an inexpressible joy of having gained some deeper, invaluable knowledge; some precious jewel of understanding which does not fade with the grey dawn and wakefulness.

. . . .

In the corner of the noisy, village pub, Owen silently nurses a pint of black stout while letting the laughter and jumbled conversation of the bar flow over and around him like waves lapping on a summer strand. A few minutes earlier, he had been engaged in deep and animated discussion with his two drinking companions regarding the positively curative merits of a certain combination of three liquors; the arguable merits of a well-known writer and poet and the unquestionable merits of the intense, dark-haired fiddler seated not ten feet away and playing his music to an inattentive audience.

The fiddler had ended one set of reels, had taken a long draught from the pint glass in front of him, replaced the glass on the table and swung into another lively set of reels.

Owen stopped his conversation and shifted his full attention to the tune the fiddler played. As the shape of the melody unfolded, Owen's concentration deepened and the shadow of a memory misted his eyes. He knew this tune. How many times had he heard it played in his lifetime? More times than he could ever calculate and yet, in a strange way, he had never heard it quite like this before.

The piece the fiddler played was the first tune Owen ever remembered hearing. His mother, Rosie, played it to him when he was no more than two of three years of age. It was one of her favourite tunes and she played it often; sometimes over and over again until she had satisfied herself that she had unravelled whatever mysteries the tune held for her.

In the five years since her death, Owen thought of Rosie often, though more often than not in connection with some difficult or unresolved aspect of their relationship. Now, amid the loud pub conversation and laughter, the fiddler's tune flooded his mind with a clarity and resonance he had not experienced before.

When the tune ended, Owen muttered some excuses to his companions, placed his half-finished drink on the table, quickly arose and pushed his way towards the door. All the way home the tune ran inside his head against a backdrop of car wheel on tarmac. It stayed with him as he made his way inside the house and fumbled for the light-switch; it stayed with him as he stirred life from dying embers inside the old iron stove. It stayed with him as he rummaged for the whiskey bottle and poured its remains into a glass and it stayed with him to dance in his brain and course through his blood with the burning liquor.

The dying fire inside the stove had come alive and Owen sat for a long while staring into its flickering heart. At last he arose and turned to the wall beside the fireplace. There, next to a faded family photograph, hung an old string-less fiddle; its wood stained brown by turf-smoke and heavy with the years.

Gently removing the instrument from the wall-hook, Owen held it as he would some delicate piece of crystal and gently ran his fingers over its aged grainy wood.

This was Rosie's fiddle. It was an old instrument when Rosie's mother, Margaret, gave it to her on her 21st birthday in the early thirties. Owen remembered Rosie often saying that it was the most valuable possession she brought with her into the house when she married Owen's father. Still cradling the fiddle, he began to hum the tune that still haunted his mind. As he softly hummed, tears welled up and began to silently fall.

Owen raised the fiddle and held it to his cheek, his tears plashing on its parched wood.

Rosie had learned to play the fiddle at her mother's knee and was, by her own account, good enough to be allowed to play with the older players at house-dances and the occasional céilí while still in her early teens. After she married Owen's father, and Owen and his brother and sister came along, the fiddle got taken out of its tattered case less often. When it did get taken out – especially at Christmas-time – the tunes would flow and Rosie's animated face would glow with happiness. In later years, when arthritis had set in to nag unpracticed fingers, she could still coax the old reels from the aged, grainy wood.

Rosie was the first to admit that, while she was not a great fiddler by the standards of the day, she could, as she said herself, "rasp out a reel, jig, hornpipe or polka" with whoever might care to sit down and play a tune with her.

"You have the music running through your veins." Her Uncle John often told her when she was still learning to play. "Isn't every one of your kith and kin a musician?" He would add proudly.

There was some truth in what Uncle John boasted of. He himself played, as did Rosie's mother – John's sister – and several of her maternal aunts, uncles and cousins. Though some played flute or concertina, it was the fiddle, which found most favour among the family musicians.

"I've heard fiddles played from Belfast to Boston." Uncle John, who had worked in America for twenty years, proclaimed often. "But do you know something? They never did sound as sweet as when played right here in Clare. And that's a fact! It's something in the clear Clare air . . . and the music being made here at home in its own place."

Fiddle playing for Uncle John was not just a pastime. It was a driving force at the centre of his being -an all-consuming passion. Rosie often told of how he would take an old wind-up Gramophone with a huge sound-horn into the meadow with him at hay-saving time. There, to the amazement of his less musically-inclined neighbours he would insist on frequent work-breaks to wind up the large black box and place upon its turntable a recently-acquired glistening, black shellac 78 RPM recording, made in far-off America by one of the legendary fiddlers such as Michael Coleman, Paddy Killoran or James Morrison. He was also prone, at the first sign of an oncoming shower, to abandoning some pressing chore in the farmyard and return indoors to take down his fiddle and practice some new tune he was intent on mastering.

Rosie adored her Uncle John who never visited the house without his fiddle tucked under his arm and when he arrived, much of the talk was of music and of the great tunes and the great players who played them.

Years after his death, Rosie still missed Uncle John's irregular visits, his tall tales and ribald stories and his hearty laugh. But most of all she missed his wild impassioned music, which seemed to her to come from somewhere deep inside his very being. For the most part his music was lively and buoyant and sometimes it was dark, sad and bitter-sweet; expressing a side to him that was completely at odds with the man's own boisterous, devil-may-care personality.

Till the end of her life, Rosie would play the tunes she had learned from him whenever she sat down to play. Sometimes, in the middle of a tune, she would halt and frown.

"What's the matter with me tonight! For the life of me I can't remember the turn of that reel as Uncle John used to play it."

She would hum the tune to herself in an attempt to recall the ebb and flow of this or that reel or jig. If the melody did not flow to her complete satisfaction, Rosie would abandon the tune and play up a slow, plaintive air.

"God be good to the dead." She would say as the tune ended, before replacing the fiddle back in its ragged case.

When Owen began to learn the fiddle from Rosie and struggled with the intricate twists and turns of Uncle John's reels, she would sometimes halt him and gently point out to him his errors and attempt to correct his clumsy, stilted playing.

"Pay attention Owen!" She would firmly say, before commencing to play her version of the piece. "The tune has to be played just as Uncle John used to play it. . . . Listen to the melody . . . feel the melody and always remember, the dead live on in the music."

Owen sat late into the night, Rosie's age-grained fiddle cradled in his lap. Outside, the grumbling winds nibbled, pinched and pushed at window, door and roof. Sitting there, he now considered how he had never before given much thought to the musical side of his mother's nature; how she valued above most things the old tunes – happy and sad – which had been passed down the generations from father to son, from mother to daughter.

Owen now tried to capture in his mind's eye an image of his mother as she played the fiddle; how she sat, how she held and seemed at one with the instrument; the delicate way her fingers moved on the strings and gripped the bow; the graceful sweeping arc of her bow -hand. Most of all he recalled how her face became transfigured as she played; utterly lost in the music that flowed from her body and soul. He tried to recall some of the stories she would tell of the tunes she played. Each tune contained a deep emotional resonance; each told a separate story; had a separate history; and each one passed down to her, no doubt, by her mother Margaret, or her Uncle John – as they would invaluable family heirlooms

These stories, Owen now realised, were as important to Rosie as the tunes themselves and even crucial to her attaining or expressing a deeper understanding of them. In the playing of the tunes and the telling and retelling of those stories surrounding them, Owen also now realised, the players released a strange power hid-

den within the notes and through them summoned long-dead kin-
folk to exist again, for however brief a time, among the living.

Over the years Owen had come to learn of the intense rever-
ence and deep regard in which the musician held the music. He
had slowly come to fully grasp the complete and sometimes desperate abandon with which players often gave themselves – body
and soul – to the sometimes irresistible lure and magical weave
of the music.

Owen gazed down at the fiddle lying on his lap. He must have
heard his mother play this fiddle hundreds of times while growing up in this house. Yet only three of those occasions now settled
in his mind's eye.

It is a lively summer's day in the late nineteen forties. In the
orchard beside the long stone farmhouse, a light breeze makes its
own soft music as it sifts through the laden apple trees and rus-
tles among the gooseberry and blackcurrant bushes.

Owen, now four years old, steers his way through the nettled,
tall grass at the orchard's edge. He is intent on capturing and
cupping in his hands a large, yellow butterfly, which now played
hide-and-seek with him among the patches of scented flock and
wild daisy by the kitchen door. He is distracted from his chase by
sounds coming from inside the house. He stops to listen to the
hum of conversation and laughter coming from within. He also
hears another sound – one he has never heard before. The butterfly hunt abandoned, and fascinated by this strange, new
sound, Owen, silent and invisible to the adults within the cool of
the house, makes his way inside and settles himself underneath
the large wooden table by the window.

From this vantage point, he knows he will be out of harm's way
and it seems to him a good place from which to observe – and to
hear – this out-of-the-ordinary event.

His mother, Rosie, is dressed in her best Sunday frock dotted
with tiny red roses on bright green stems and is seated between
her mother, Margaret, and her uncle John; his large, portly figure shaking with mirth at the telling of one of his stories. Each
holds a fiddle and bow and even amid the animated talk and
laughter, they pluck and bow the strings with a fierce urgency.

To Owen's ears, it is a cacophony of tense, excited sound from
within a forest of darting arms, flicking wrists and arcing fiddle-
bows.

Suddenly, and without warning, the loud talk and laughter is quieted. Three fiddles are raised in unison, tucked under chins and three bows deftly fall on taut, finely tuned strings. As if by command of the darting bows, there flows from the fiddles a keen, hard-edged sound, which rises and swirls about the room. Soon, the air all about him is charged with the energy of music. The tunes – though complex – are woven by the players with ease and grace; the notes, invisible amber and gold kites, anchored to the earth by feet tapping a steady, hypnotic tattoo on the stone floor.

Owen remains where he is – still, silent and quiet – seated on a table-rung. From here he gazes up at the three figures seated in a half-circle on the kitchen floor.

He remains for a long while seated underneath the table; held in the thrall of the strange, wild sound of three fiddles weaving their sure pathways through this new – though somehow familiar – music.

Owen studies the player's faces. All three have their eyes closed: shutting out all but the music they are creating. Uncle John and Margaret wear frowns of earnest concentration. Only Rosie, Owen notices, is smiling as she plays.

Owen was to hear that same wild sound over a decade later. He is now fourteen; a surly, dismissive teenager more interested in rock 'n roll and electric guitars than fiddles and fiddle-players.

It is evening in late autumn and a bleak wind continues to strip the apple trees of their burdens. His mother Rosie, her auburn hair now flecked with grey, is seated next to Margaret who plucks at fiddle strings with aged – though still delicate – bony fingers. Uncle John is missing, dead these last two years. Taking his place in the semi-circle is Owen's younger sister, Nóirín, who sits beside Rosie and quietly rosins her bow. The conversation is quiet and sparse, the laughter muted, the voices low and intimate. The talk is of Aunt Brigid, Margaret's sister, who has not long since died.

"She was the one with the music . . . sure it poured out of her . . . like milk from a jug. Brigid put us all . . . even John . . . in the ha'penny place. And as for that old concertina she played! Sure that was held together with string but she could make it laugh and she could make it cry. When she was on form, Lord but she made the auld thing look as if it was dancing in her two hands."

Margaret's eyes were shiny-wet. "Do you know she would dream up the music while she slept? She often told me she would often wake suddenly in the dark of the night with some strange tune running around in her head. Right away she would get out of her bed, light a candle and write the music down, while it was still fresh and before it went from her mind . . . as dreams do. She would write the music on the wallpaper next to the bed-head with a pencil tied to a twine attached to the bedpost. Sure the entire wall on her side of the bed was covered in music notes . . . her dreams scribbled up there for her to play in the cold light of morning. Do you remember, Rosie? You saw it yourself at her wake . . . the wall beside her bed covered with music. Before I said goodbye to her, I peeled a scrap of wallpaper off the wall . . . I still have it safe at home. Ah yes! but she was the one with the music."

Memory-laden silence hangs for a moment in the air; broken only by fiddle strings being softly plucked. Finally Margaret sighs, brightens and begins to speak of a letter she has recently received from distant relations in America trying to trace their Irish roots.

"Sure, I didn't even know they existed 'till the letter arrived. But I suppose I should write back to them soon." She chuckles.

"There might even be a legacy on the way. Then I could buy myself a better fiddle. This auld yoke has seen better days."

She lightly raps the fiddle with the bow. A shower of rosin falls from the bow-hairs to rest like snow at the base of the bridge.

A string barks out a harsh note in response.

"I swear Adam himself played this old fiddle while Eve danced!" Margaret throws her head back and laughs heartily. Owen notices how like Uncle John she is at that moment.

Tucking the fiddle underneath her chin, Margaret nods to Rosie and Nóirín.

"Do you remember this one, Rosie? Brigid and John loved to play it." Margaret begins to play an old tune, teasing out the notes as if testing their willingness to be played today in this setting. Rosie and Nóirín gently follow the swell and flow of the tune. The three fiddles search for a moment to lock on the rhythm and pulse as the old reel unfolds its shape and form. Soon the three fiddles are as one; merged in a single sound that is at once taut, high and lonesome. To Owen, the music they make is as wild and free as he recalls it from that other remembered day more than a decade earlier.

Now, again, he watches the three fiddlers; instruments tucked under chins, eyes closed in deep concentration as hands draw graceful bows over rosin-dusted strings and he hears again the old reels flow in musical conversation through three generations.
Only his sister Nóirín, Owen notices, is smiling.

St. Stephen's Day morning had dawned seasonably bitter, misty and damp. Following his customary Christmas day celebrations, Owen, feeling all of his forty-plus years, slept late. It was his first Christmas spent in this tiny cottage nestled among the sky-grey rocks and hazel-bushes, some miles from the house in which he was born and reared. More than a quarter of a century had passed since he had departed the locality to make his own way in the world. Now, a little battle-scarred and world-weary, he was happy to be home again and to live alone for a time in this tiny, secluded cottage.

Having finally shaken off the cobwebs of a mild hangover, Owen pottered about the house for most of the day, drinking strong coffee, reading and chopping wood to feed the fire in his large, open-hearth fireplace. From time to time, he set his book aside to go to the door and peer expectantly into the silent mist.

Yesterday he had celebrated the Christian Christmas festival but today he awaited an event which would mark the beginning of the pre-Christian mid-winter celebrations – the expected arrival in his house of the 'Wren Boys'; also know as 'Mummers'

From first to last light, these gaily-attired, merry bands of masked musicians and dancers roved the country highways and byways each St. Stephen's Day as they had done for several generations. Their purpose was to visit as many households, in as many parishes as possible, to play out on every stone floor and hearth a ritual of the Pagan Winter Solstice – far more ancient than the one celebrated on the previous day.

Darkness fell early and its thickening gloom matched Owen's mood precisely. As six o'clock approached, his agitation grew to disappointment. Not to be visited by at least one of these groups of Wrenboys on this day was considered to be unlucky and a portent of ill-luck for the year to come. Disconsolate, he stared into the blazing fire. For whatever reason, he now admitted to himself, he had been by-passed, or – worse still!! – forgotten, by the several wandering troupes of local Wrenboys.

Suddenly, and without warning, the cottage door was flung

open to admit a group of four be-ribboned masked Mummers.

A delighted Owen jumped to his feet.

"Welcome! You're welcome to my house!" Owen said, clearing a space for the silent colourful visitors. "I'd given up on you."

Without uttering a word, the mysterious figures rush by him to take command of the floor and commence a spirited dance to the music of a lone. slightly stooped fiddler; masked and partially hidden in the half-light by the doorway. The tune they dance to is an old reel which Owen recognised; while also noting that the masked fiddler played it haltingly, as if struggling to recall the tune's complex twists and turns.

Suddenly the tune and dance is ended and as swiftly and silently as the group arrive, they depart the house: melting into the misty blackness of this pagan night.

They are gone but they leave behind an atmosphere now charged with a new energy – a strange magic – created by their presence, their music and their dance which resonates in the room long after their departure. For a long time, Owen stands bathed in the lingering aura and feeling his spirit cleansed, his house sanctified.

Later than evening, Owen set out to visit his mother, He arrived to find Rosie in the company of his sister Nóirín, and three of her friends. It was a family gathering where Christmas cheer was the central guest, with hot ports and whiskeys being prepared and plates of cold turkey and hams being consumed with great relish around a blazing fire.

"Did you have any visit from the Wren Boys?" Rosie inquired, stirring a spoon of sugar into her hot port.

"I did." Owen replied. "A last minute call from a group of four . . . and a fiddler."

"Were they any craic?" Nóirín's friend Tessa asked.

"Oh, the dancers were OK . . . a bit wooden . . . but not bad . . . as dancers go."

"What about the fiddler?" Rosie asked.

"The fiddler?" Owen replied. "Not that bad I suppose . . . certainly no Tommy Peoples. I don't know where they unearthed him."

"Him! Him! What makes you think it was a 'him'?" Rosie retorted with a laugh and turned to the fireside gathering "Do ye hear that! He didn't even recognise his own mother's fiddle-play-

ing! And you're supposed to be a judge of music and musicians!!
Some judge! Humph!"

All eyes turned on Owen as everyone laughed, waiting for the
penny – and Owen's jaw – to drop. When it did, Owen could but
raise his glass to them all and laughed heartily with them. His
visiting 'mystery' group of Wren-boy Mummers were none other
than his own family – now here gathered – and who, at the last
minute and at Rosie's suggestion, had decided to don the traditional Wren-boy garb and masks and visit a few near neighbours
– and especially Owen – for a bit of Christmas diversion.

Rosie, who had not played a note for well over a decade, had
taken down her dusty old fiddle, tuned its slackened strings,
rosined the yellowed bow, donned her Mummers mask and headed off with the group into the deepening night to partake in this
most ancient of Winter Solstice rituals.

On her return, she slackened the fiddle-strings and hung the
fiddle and bow on the wall by the fireplace. She never took down
or played the fiddle ever again.

The fire in the stove had died to a mat of dimly glowing
embers. Owen shivered in the room's late-night chill.

"Must have drifted." he said to himself and stiffly arose from
the chair and stood facing the stone-arched fireplace. "It's late."

He stretched and glanced at the clock on the near wall; whose
steadfast pendulum had beaten a steady rhythm to his mother's
life in this house – and which now beat time to his life and the
tune still haunting his mind.

He had dreamed and in his dream he saw a young, red-haired,
smiling woman with a fiddle tucked beneath her chin. The dream
slowly unfolded and he saw the same woman, now middle-aged,
seated between her daughter and her own mother; their three
fiddles ringing clear and their bow-arms and fingers dancing in
unison to a familiar tune.

That image dissolved and now he saw an old fiddler – shadowy,
stooped and masked – by an open door on a mid-winter's night,
playing a tune from the heart that wrenched and tugged and
called out to the very depths of his soul.

The masked, mysterious fiddler played an old familiar reel –
just as Rosie and her mother Margaret and her Uncle John would
have played it – bittersweet, sad and melancholy.

Stillness

In perfect stillness
I stand, bewitched
in the afterglow of evening birdsong.
Lingering, rippling
the hem of twilight's summer cloak.
I taste the air
dripping from the blue-black
bowl of night,
perfumed with turf-smoke,
soft voices and a piper's tune.
A cuckoo calls
and I am liquid.

In velvet quiet,
I stand enthralled.
I am not surprised
to find the moon
wear a face
that was mine
before my ancestors lived.
Neither
am I surprised
to find
I am the moon
and I am shining.

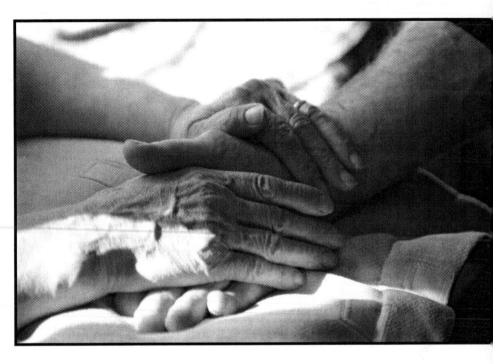

The Death of Martin McCann

I**T WASN'T SO DIFFICULT AFTER ALL – THIS** dying business. Everybody, Martin accepted, had to go sometime and he was, at this moment, fully prepared for his imminent and unavoidable face-to-face encounter with the Dark Angel. What surprised him most was, after all he had heard, read or imagined about this most dreaded moment, nothing had prepared him for what he now experienced. There was no unbearable, body-racking pain; as he had fully expected there would be at his time of dying. Neither was there any gnawing body-ache or physical discomfort. It was as if his body had passed beyond all the ills of the mortal state.

There was no celestial music either. No bright, beckoning light at the end of a long, dark tunnel and neither, he registered with some degree of surprise, was there any trace or apprehension of fear as he lay, utterly still and quiet between clean, fresh sheets, within his ever-decreasing cone of life.

Fear, he thought – like all unfettered human passions – was for young men.

Now, as he lay here, even that emotion – like the minutes, hours and days of his life – had fled his mortal body. The circle of his life was about to close and become complete. To Martin, at this very moment, his dying seemed to make perfect sense.

In this same bed, in which he had been conceived and born, in this same house, where he had grown to manhood, Martin McCann was preparing to die. Not that he felt sick enough to die. His pneumonia, brought on by a bone-chilling wetting earned from a night on the mountainside watching lambing sheep had left him with high temperatures and sapped his wiry body of all strength and resistance. Otherwise he felt no great discomfort.

Nevertheless, he knew his time had come. He just knew it. Not from his head or brain but from somewhere deep inside his blood and bones came this new and final self-knowledge.

"Eighty -five years!" Martin said gently to himself. "Not a bad run. Not a bad run at all!"

He had clocked up a greater tally of years that did either of his parents and he had outlived his three brothers by several years. Now he was bone-tired and world-weary and ready for the long sleep ahead. All he had to do for that sleep to come, was to will it – but not yet . . . not yet. Not until he reached out for it to embrace him, or the final sleep came to claim him.

To fully experience life, Martin had long ago come to realise, was that a human being be fully conscious of Self and the world into which one had been born. Life was about feeling and experiencing. Death, he also knew, was the absolute absence of both.

In these final moments left to him, he thought, and for as long as he was conscious, he would fully enjoy and experience this feeling of lassitude, which covered him as completely as his own skin. It was a feeling that teased and tugged at his spirit to give itself to the waves of beckoning blackness now lapping at the corners of his ebbing consciousness. But for as long as he might, so he determined, he would hover in this comfortable neither-world of both being and non-being.

Martin McCann was not without regrets about leaving this life. He would miss leaving forever his beloved hills, vales and woods, the wild rocky places and the sheltering sky, which had nourished both body and spirit since his youth. Most of all he would miss Nora, his wife. He knows also that she would miss him and his soul was heavy at the thought of leaving her behind on this, his final journey.

Martin became aware of a numbness, which crept slowly over him like an invisible mist. Though his legs and lower body no longer seemed part of him, he also became aware that his mind and senses at this moment were more acute than ever. Now, the very air about him seemed charged with an energy and electricity he had not experienced before.

Without moving his head, he could hear the night breeze flow like honey over ancient stones on the hillside and on down the hill to his orchard. He could hear it rustle through the tall grass and whisper between the blackcurrant and apple-trees. His eyes glistened with tears. He would never again taste the fruit of those trees or sit again beneath their leafy shade.

Breathing deeply, Martin could scent the very bowels of the night wafting in from outside his window. He breathed in the scent of blossom from the hawthorn bushes a good mile away and so too the intoxicating fragrance of the rose trees Nora planted on their first days living together in the old stone cottage.

"How beautiful!" he thought. "And how strange!" Though it was early winter and the scent of whitethorn and rose-blossom now wafted through the room, Martin knew that neither tree could still be in blossom. Yet his senses were so filled with their heady wild essence, it was as if his face was buried deep in their best summer finery.

He stilled his breathing and listened. He listened as never before. He listened to the voice of the wind and the rain falling softly on the mountainside; to the sound of the stones, to the winged poetry and music of unseen night-birds; to the 'click-clack' of the cricket in the open hearth below-stairs in the kitchen. He listened for, and imagined he could hear, the spider spinning his web and to all the world's hidden creatures.

"Beautiful!" he sighed. "So beautiful!"

Now, finally, he understood the poetry of it all. The glorious Life-song, which Nature had sung to him all his days of living. Though he had tried all his life to listen, though sometimes he had ignored, or failed to hear – to truly hear – or understand Her glorious Canticle. Now as the end approached – like an old and trusty friend – Mother Nature had come to him with these gifts, to bid him a last farewell. But perhaps it was just his mind play-ing tricks on him. Or was it the many voices of his God, calling him home? To Martin, it all now seemed to make perfect sense – just like his dying.

Without opening his eyes he could see, even through his bed-room roof, the vast canopy of a star-strewn sky stretch away to a distant horizon. He heard the swish of a star falling close by, leav-ing in its wake a fiery trail spangled with the stardust of his eighty-five short years of living. In the far distance he could hear the sound he had awaited – the high-pitched zinging of this new dawn breaking. This, he also knew from deep within, would be a special dawn – his last on this earth.

Slowly, his eyes and lips opened to receive the sacrament of its light and life and he breathed deeply of it.

From the kitchen downstairs, there came the sound of Nora slowly moving about preparing her breakfast and a cup of black, sugarless tea for her husband. She had sat with him in vigil throughout this long, black night. From midnight, until she left him to prepare breakfast, she held his hand as if it were a mortal anchor. During that time they did not speak – nor did they have to. In these quiet hours it seemed as if their minds were as one and their innermost feelings ran back and forth through their intertwined fingers like an electrical current. In these hours too, their bony old fingers silently recited to each other the Great Hymn of their sixty-odd years together as man and wife.

In the dim glow of the night-light, Nora could not see Martin's lips but she knew he was smiling. Though she knew her husband's time with her was short, she was resigned and ready to accept God's will. In a strange way, she thought, it had not been like this since their wedding night. As the night hours had passed, so unraveled the mysteries and markers of their lifetime together, the quarrels, the passions, joys and sorrows, the distances and the closeness between them down the years.

Most of all there was the wondrous mystery of their three children – shot like arrows from the supple bow of their love. The children were grown now and only Sonny – who last night had driven to collect his sisters, Maeve and Ellen, from Dublin where they both worked – had stayed on the homestead to carry on the work that had engaged his ancestors for generations – that of sheep farming in this remote part of the Burren.

Martin's breath now came in deep, long sighs. Yes, he would miss Nora, Sonny and Maeve and Ellen too. But Sonny and the others were young and would forget – eventually. But what of Nora – would she forget? She had often said that she hoped she would be taken before him and she would not – could not – live on without her other-half. Now she was not going to get her wish.

"I'm sorry, Nora. I wish . . . I wish . . ." Martin spoke but there was no sound.

Downstairs in the kitchen, Nora poured steaming hot water from the boiling kettle onto fresh tealeaves in the rose-embossed crock teapot. This was the teapot Martin had given her one Christmas – fifteen, maybe twenty years ago and she only used it for special occasions. This morning she reached for it automatically. Nora was bone tired from her long night-vigil, but she would rest later, when Sonny and the girls returned. She had watched over her husband in his past illnesses down the years, but this, she knew, was different and she wore the weight of it as a heavy yoke.

Martin was almost gone, she sensed it, and only the warmth of his hand in hers indicated the flame of life – though flickering low – still burned within his breast. Maybe . . . the thought struck her, maybe if she lay next to him he would absorb some of her vital life-flame and from it suck what strength he would need to fight his way back to her. She quickly filled Martin's teacup with fresh tea and laid it on a tray as the painted traces of dawn's first light shimmered in the east.

"Nora!" Martin's voice floated down from above like a sudden snow-shower.

The tray slipped from her hands and scattered its contents on the stone kitchen floor. She ran to the stairs, stiffly clambered the steps to the landing and stumbled, breathless, into their bedroom.

Martin lay in exactly the same position as when she had left him. His urgent hand reached out and she ran to grasp it.

"I'm here, Martin! It's alright! I'm here with you."

Nora quickly removed her dressing gown, flung the bed-covers back and lay down beside him on the bed. His breathing was at first laboured, then becoming shorter and shallower until she could barely sense the rhythm and pulse of it.

Martin felt the familiar press of her body against his and felt her body-heat caress and warm his chilled skin. He hovered in a dream-like state, his spirit willing him to let go the bonds of wakefulness. He felt he could at last immerse himself in the inviting pool of sleep and give himself utterly to the sound of water gently lapping at the edge of his enveloping darkness. The invisible fingers of ice and fire, which probed and penetrated his abdomen and lower chest finally reached his heart and squeezed.

A single, final breath left his body to utter her name one last time.

"Nora." Fluttering like a freed sparrow, her name rose from Martin's lips.

When Sonny, Maeve and Ellen returned to the house later that morning they found them both, peaceful, childlike and smiling, like sleeping lovers.

All Souls Night

Days of skeletal emotions
the weather-blistered
countryside
signals its coming.
This primal night
of fear and dread
falls at last
on cold, wet stone
and crow-racked garden.
I am ten autumns old,
yet the unimaginable
business performed this night,
chills and drains
my blood and bones.
Evening dies quickly,
waked by steel-blue clouds
and chattering magpies.
I gaze upwards;
the sky, thick and starless,
gives no comfort.

Almost time to go to church!
A sullen fire
spits sparked messages
from those suffering souls
waiting for release below.
   Hurry! Hurry!
Window-panes creak and groan;
the unknown
raps loudly; the unseen
stares.
I shuffle and juggle

with soap and comb,
leather and a boot-lace;
until, too soon,
it is time to go.

Then they rise in me,
images; tortured, agonised.
Images that crowd
my racing imagination.
How many souls
will my childish prayers release
before I go to sleep
tonight?
Do souls have eyes?
Does my soul see me?
And if I die
before I wake,
will mine go down
to burn with them
and await my turn
next All Soul's Night?

We set out,
my brother and I;
false courage filling
overcoat pockets.
We trudge
through the whispering gloom
to the waiting church.
From the gate,
it looks tomb-like;
shadowy, hollow, final.
Blinking, I peer
into its cavernous belly.
From the door
its emptyness is crushing.

Shadows
take human shape.
Sounds
take prayer word.

Hail Mary! Holy Mary!
 Save us! Save us!
No turning back now.
I creep in silence
into the waxen glow
of funeral-candle flickerings
to kneel and wait
and watch
an old man, toothless,
work-worn,
wiping glistening hail
from his Sunday cap.
Gazing glass-eyed
at a chipped chalk icon,
an old woman, death faced,
kneels; crow-bone fingers
shuffle and twitch;
rosary beads knit and purl
Embroidered placations.
 Hail Mary! Holy Mary!
 Pray for us! Pray for us!
Footsteps
echo and ring;
noses
sniff and scent
the acrid incensed air;
beads and bones
rattle and drum.
The ritual has commenced.
 Jesus falls the first time!

Furtively, I peer
at a mottled wall.
Dark and faded,
the Stations of the Cross
peer back.
 Jesus falls the Second Time.
Sighs, mingled
with yellow candle smoke
and endless, wordless chanting
float

Jesus falls the Third Time.
to rest eternal
among prayer-stained rafters.

Outside, the wind stirs
new terrors
as I race my rounds.
One soul, two souls,
ten souls saved!
In the half-light
a cold rain stings and burns.
Grim-faced pilgrims moving;
unconscious players
in some eternal mime.
I gaze upwards,
a star winks
and is gone.
I walk quickly
away from this place.
    Don't look behind!
Dead leaves and gravel converse
and crunch
under polished boots.
We speed homeward,
my brother and I, to light and life
and the safety
of hot buttered scones.
There, at last, the weight
is lifted; the dread
is swallowed
by warm kitchen smells
and a mother's eyes.

An hour ago
I was old as Death.
Now again, I am ten
and my blood runs red
and shadows and spirits
and long-dead faces
are quickly banished.
Now life and play

and laughter
fill the night hours
'till sleep comes creeping;
this All Souls Night.

The Stone Goddess

Winner of the 2005
Bram Stoker Gothic Short Story Award

"There are more things in heaven and earth, Horatio, than are dreamt of in your philosophy."
Shakespeare's Hamlet: Act 1, Scene 5.

The Bard of Avon knew that there are some things in this world that are not fully understood and are best left alone. There are some things in this world that harbour secrets that are not for the human eye or ear; secrets so deep and dark, so ancient and terrible that man – should he meddle carelessly or pry too closely – could be utterly destroyed. There are many people who do not fully understand this strange law of Nature; or indeed, Supernature.

This is a story of two such men.

I T IS MORNING IN JACK KAVANAGH'S BED & Breakfast Guest House on the west coast of Clare. As he went about his usual morning tasks, Jack paused for a moment at the kitchen window to survey the Atlantic Ocean that spread before him like a vast blue-gray blanket.

"It certainly is rough today." He thought, his eyes following the wild, white horses as they bolted landward before smashing themselves on a foaming shore.

"There will be a storm before evening, for sure" He said to nobody in particular. His eyes then fell on a squat, stone building a few hundred yards to the southwest that nestled in an exposed and tree-less hollow between his house and seashore. This ancient – and now abandoned – church-graveyard of St. Ronan had been the site of Pilgrimage for local people for centuries.

Now, as the dark, gray clouds gathered on the distant horizon, Kavanagh was struck by how lonely the church looked – surrounded as it was by a tangle of mossy, weather-beaten old gravestones – on this All Souls Eve; the first day of winter.

The hum of conversation from the dining room drew Jack Kavanagh back to the business of the day. It was obvious to Jack, as he served breakfast to his two guests that they were not in the best of spirits. Phil O'Carroll and Joe McCarthy – both Civil Servant Officials from the Department of Monuments – were regular visitors to Kavanagh's 'Sea-View' Guesthouse in the course of their work; which took them to all parts of the country.

They had arrived from Dublin the previous evening and after small talk with Kavanagh and his wife Brigid, and a few pints in the local pub, they had retired for the night. They were down awaiting breakfast in the dining room before eight o'clock; earlier than Kavanagh had seen them up before and now they sat speaking in hushed tones as he prepared their breakfasts in the kitchen.

"Good morning, Mr. O'Carroll . . . Mr. McCarthy . . . and how are ye this morning, gentlemen?" Kavanagh brightly inquired while setting plates of sizzling rasher, egg and sausage in front of the two men.

"Hale and hearty? I trust ye both slept well."

The older of the two men, Phil O'Carroll, remained silent as he sat and stared vacantly at the plate placed before him.

"Ahhh, I . . . ah . . . we've been better Jack. We've been better. I can't say I slept at all well last night for some reason."

It was Joe McCarthy who spoke, scrunching up his bony face while running his fingers through his bushy black beard. "And neither did Mr. O'Carroll . . . right Phil?"

"Humph! I've had better nights." O'Carroll mumbled and continued to peer disconsolately at the place in front of him. Kavanagh began to laugh but stopped short at a black, sideways glare from O'Carroll.

"Poor sleepers eh? Well, I can see the red eyes on the pair of ye. Oh, probably nothing more than too much cheese before bed, you know they do say cheese before bed causes nightmares . . . or a bad pint perhaps?"

Kavanagh offered reassuringly. "A touch of the 'morning after', I expect. You'll both be as right as rain when you get a good breakfast inside you and get out into the air . . . take a walk down by the sea maybe. Nothing like good country air to clear away the cobwebs I always say."

"Oh no!" McCarthy prodded his fried-egg absentmindedly. "I can assure you Jack, it wasn't cheese . . . or the few pints . . . it was that bloody dog of yours! Jeez, the beast howled outside my window half the Goddamn night. At one stage, I thought it was going to get into the room to me. Don't get me wrong . . . I like dogs. I have a dog . . . but a vicious dog like that!! . . . should be kept locked up . . . chained even. I hardly slept a wink." McCarty scowled and continued to prod the now-runny egg white.

"A dog? . . . howling?" Kavanagh's voice registered surprise. "My dog? That can't be! . . . I don't even own a dog. Oh, we had a harmless mutt a few years back but he got run over by a lorry out on the road."

"Well somebody around here has a dog . . . because it kept me from my sleep as well! How could you not have heard it? It must have waked half the parish . . . you must have heard it! Oh yes, there was a dog all right . . . because I saw the bloody beast. . . and it looked to me like a . . . a killer! McCarthy's right." O'Carroll's knuckles whitened as he tightened his grip on his knife and fork. "It howled half the night below in the yard there. I saw it paw at my window. It damn near pushed in the windowpane. I never saw a dog as big in my life . . . like a . . . a bloody wolfhound it was! You must have heard it? It howled so as to wake the dead! Damn animal kept me from my sleep."

"I honestly never heard a thing . . ." Kavanagh looked at the men in disbelief. ". . . and neither did Brigid! She's a light sleeper and would have mentioned it if she did. Oh, there are dogs in the neighbourhood . . . sheepdogs . . . mutts . . . mongrels . . . and so forth . . . but no big dogs . . . no Alsatians or such . . . like the one you described. Are you sure you didn't dream it all?"

"It was no dream! How could Joe and I . . . the both of us . . . have the same dream? It was definitely no dream, I'm sure of that! I don't know where it came from . . . but there was a dog out there last night . . . for sure!"

"Or a wolf . . ." McCarthy said quietly to himself and shot a glance at his colleague.

"A wolf? In these parts? Now I know you have been dreaming." Jack Kavanagh laughed a hard, nervous laugh.

Phil O'Carroll suddenly remembered he did indeed have a dream – an extremely disturbing dream. Now, in the early morning light, he frowned as the shadow of its memory crept across his face like a dark cloud.

He had gone to bed the previous night – happy and relaxed after his visit to the pub – and had slipped quickly into an uneasy sleep. His dream now returned to his mind as clear and real as that dog he had seen at his window in the misty moonlight. It had been a truly terrifying dream; like none he had ever dreamed before.

In the dream, he lay on a bed – or stone slab – in a shapeless room in utter, inky darkness. It was darkness so deep, so black that he could not fathom it and it weighed oppressively on him. He slowly became aware of being watched by eyes peering intensely from the inky blackness. With a sense of growing dread, he felt his body being crushed by their willful ferocity.

Only then did he become aware that he was trapped in the fetters of a dream, a dream from which he desperately had to escape. He tried to move his hands and his feet, but could not move a muscle. From afar, yet close by, he heard voices – women's voices – at first whispering, then wailing and anguished, then loud and angry. He struggled to come awake. He struggled so violently it seemed as if his heart would rip asunder from the strain of his exertions. When he did come awake – heart pounding like an African drum – he heard the forlorn howl of a dog from beneath his outside window-ledge.

It took many minutes before he could fully compose himself and for the remainder of the night he lay awake awaiting the first light of a welcome dawn.

Now seated at breakfast, he shuddered again at the memory of the dream. The strange thing, he now pondered in the cold light of morning, was that his colleague, McCarthy, had had the same dream.

Just a coincidence?

"Very strange!" O'Carroll muttered into his teacup. "Very strange indeed."

"Oh, it was a dog all right!" McCarthy said, his voice became hard and sharp, like frozen ice. "A flesh and blood dog . . . bared fangs . . . this length! . . . slobbering at the window . . . it was a good job it was closed. Most definitely a dog! As Mr. O'Carroll says, that dog was no bloody dream, I can tell you that!"

Shaking his head in sympathy, Jack Kavanagh decided that it was best to change the subject.

"Tchh! Tchh! I'm sorry this has caused you both some discomfort. I'll check out this dog business right away. Anyway, ye're both up and about. . . and tucking into a good breakfast . . . that's the main thing, I always say. What's on the menu for you both today?"

McCarthy perked up a little at Kavanagh's enquiry.

"Well Jack, we have to visit a few historic sites in the area. You know . . . the usual . . . ring forts, castles, standing stones. . . that sort of thing. All in a day's work."

"Ah yes, we have a busy day ahead of us, between one thing and another." O'Carroll seemed eager to shake off the gloom he had shared with his assistant and was now willing to join in the conversation. "We have alot of work on our plate this time of year . . . and, by the way Jack, we'll be back here again tonight. In fact, we'll be working in the graveyard down the road there when we get through with our other business."

"Oh! . . . and what will you be working at there?" Kavanagh's voice registered surprise.

O'Carroll sipped from his teacup, leaned back in his chair and said in a low tone. "Well, I'll tell you Jack. But I'll ask you not to breath a word to a soul. The less the locals know of our work . . ." He gestured toward the window. ". . . the easier our job is all round. We've come to remove something from St Ronan's Church that should have been removed years ago."

"Oh? . . . And what's that?" Kavanagh commenced clearing the breakfast plates from the table.

"We've come for the Sheela. We're taking the Sheela-na-Gig back to Dublin with us."

Kavanagh's smile faded. He slowly repeated what O'Carroll had just said, "You're . . . taking . . . the Sheela-na-Gig? . . . away? . . . to Dublin? You're joking, surely!"

He sounded as if he had not heard O'Carroll correctly.

The stone Sheela-na-Gig carving had looked down from the ivy-covered wall above the main door at the south- facing side of the church for as long as the church had stood there; which was over a thousand years at least. Nobody alive really knew how ancient the weatherworn effigy was – two thousand years – perhaps double that age, maybe more.

The 'Sheela-na-Gigs' were known to be of Celtic Pagan origin. They had been adored as 'Earth Mother' figures – fertility Goddesses in pre and post-Christian Ireland. Similar stone 'Sheela's' – also called Eostre, Cybele, Isis, Gaia, Beltis, Kali and Ashteroth – were formidable, often terrible, Goddesses in other ancient cultures. They were to be found in certain parts of England and France and even on ancient Hindu temples in India and the middle-east.

How this particular pagan Goddess (the ancient Cow Goddess known as 'Boand') came to sit in her hunched position – her genitalia exposed for all to see – over the entrance-door of the now-ruined and abandoned Christian Church, was an eternal mystery.

Many locals believed the carving to be that of an early, nameless Christian martyr. Others believed She had the power to make childless women fertile. It was a known fact that barren women would come in the dead of night to act out some ancient ritual in front of the grotesque stone effigy; as had countless of childless women for at least a thousand years before the coming of Christianity.

Nobody had dared . . . or ever would dare . . . remove the Sheela from Her ivy-adorned throne or tamper with Her in anyway during Her ten century-long, silent vigil.

"That's right! The dear old Sheela herself. We've come to take the sweet old lady on a little trip to the big city." O'Carroll said patronizingly, dabbing his napkin about his egg-stained chin. "And not before time, I think. Her Ladyship is going to be given a face-lift and brush-up and exhibited at the Museum next month. Mind you, in my book, it should have been removed from public view long ago! I mean to say! . . . It's nothing more than

pornographic . . . a pornographic stone carving! There are actually people who believe that stuff like this is . . . art . . . high art
even!!!" O'Carroll fairly spat out his words.

"But I'll tell you what it is. It's a . . . a . . . pagan, devilish abom-
ination . . . that's what it is. And above the door of a church . . . a
CHRISTIAN CHURCH at that! What kind of Christians put it up
in the first place, explain that . . . if you can!"

Kavanagh's face registered both shock and incredulity.

"You're removing the . . . the . . . Sheela-na-Gig from the
church?" He interrupted. "But it's been there for . . . God knows
how long?"

With eyes ablaze, O'Carroll now warmed fully to his topic.

"Oh, that's as may be. But I ask you again, how in God's name
was she tolerated . . . then or now? As far as I'm concerned, it's a
bit like putting a nude Marilyn Monroe . . . or Sharon Stone . . .
above the door of a modern church. It beggars belief so it does!
Well, my instructions are clear. I'm to take her from that wall and
take her to Dublin where she's to be shown to some European and
American historians and then consigned to the Museum base-
ment to join the rest of her disgusting stone relatives. Humph! If
I had my way the revolting thing would be smashed to
smithereens. In my book, pornography is pornography . . . even if
it is several thousand years old. Anyway, Joe and I have to obey
Head-office brass. They say take it down from the wall and cart
it back to Dublin and that's exactly what we plan to do tomorrow."

Visible excited by his superior's impassioned outburst,
McCarthy vigorously nodded in agreement and added, "And we
don't want any messing . . . like that business back in the sixties
. . . when a few local boyos removed an old standing stone and
kept it hidden rather than see it disappear to some Art Exhibition
in Dublin. Do you remember that? . . . made the papers. . . and
the TV. . . so it did! So there you have it Jack. Time to wave 'bye
bye' to your sexy Sheela. Though I doubt if anyone will miss her
. . . or even care she's gone."

"Ok. Joe . . . cut the comedy." O' Carroll rose from the table and
moved to the hallway to don a fur-lined anorak.

"We've a busy schedule in front of us and it's going to be a
nippy day, I'd say. The evenings are closing in too. It's All Souls
Eve tonight, isn't it? We'll have to make it back to the church
down the road by five-thirty latest, if we're to get her ladyship

from her pedestal before nightfall. We should be done by six . . .
six-thirty . . . but if we're not . . . keep the dinner warm for us
Jack. Oh, and by the way, we'll need garage space to store the
Sheela 'till we leave for Dublin in the morning. Ok Joe, lets get
moving! See you later Jack."

The two men, gathering up briefcases and maps, headed for
the door; leaving Kavanagh to mull over the startling news that
the Sheela-na-Gig was to be finally removed from Her natural
place overlooking the bones and stones of Her graveyard
Kingdom. She must have witnessed some strange comings and
goings during Her centuries staring down from above the church
door.

This disturbing news of Her imminent departure left
Kavanagh with an uneasy feeling in the pit of his stomach as he
went about his morning's work.

The late autumn air had hung heavy all day. Gathering clouds
to the west and south promised rain, which never came. As an
early dusk fell, the sky now filled with rooks, crows and sea-birds;
wings flapping homeward.

Jack Kavanagh had forgotten about his two guests; until he
glanced from the dining-room window and saw their Range Rover
parked outside the church-graveyard. It was now well past five
o'clock and almost dark.

"I see O'Carroll and McCarthy are busy at their work." He said
to himself. He sighed and shook his head. He somehow did not
feel at ease with what the two men were about to do. The Sheela-
na-Gig had not been disturbed for centuries and it did not seem
to him right or proper that the two men -without any local debate
or argument – take Her down from Her resting place and spirit
Her away to Dublin. He wished they had not informed him about
their plans. That way, he would not feel this uneasy, nagging feeling deep in his gut that he should be doing something, informing
somebody. But they are Civil Servants, he reasoned, obeying
orders, and their superiors must be correct in their decision to
remove the statue.

Still, he had to admit, the whole affair bothered him greatly.
He thought no more of it and joined Brigid to help out in the
kitchen.

"Do you know what it is, Jack, you can feel the winter chill
already. It's gotten much colder all of a sudden, don't you think?"

Brigid removed a tray of fresh, hot scones from the kitchen range. "And just listen to those crows, will you! I've never heard them so disturbed. They're certainly making quite a racket. Is something happening out there?"

Kavanagh, having finished dicing vegetables, moved to the kitchen window and peered into the darkness.

From nearby, he heard the shrill squawking of crows, rooks and seagulls

"You're right . . . those birds are upset about something. Lets have a look. It's black as pitch out there."

As he squinted through the misted glass, the now-piercing din of shrieking birds filled his ears. The sound was followed by another high-pitched sound, this time a blood-curdling scream.

Kavanagh frantically wiped the mist off the windowpane and pressed his face close to the glass. As he peered out into the gloom, yet another terror-laden scream filled the air; this time followed by a howl, which chilled him to the marrow. It was a sound that had come from no human throat.

"God in heaven! What in God's name is that?" He turned to his wife who stood – ashen faced – by the kitchen table. "Brigid, did you hear that? . . . or did I imagine it?"

"I heard it too, Jack . . . merciful God! Something has happened." Brigid paled and clutched at the medallion at her throat. "Somebody's in trouble out there . . . an accident . . . a car-crash maybe? It might be a neighbour . . . or Mr. O'Carroll or Mr. McCarthy! Jack, You'll have to go out there and see what's wrong!"

"Your right . . . quick! Where's the torch? God almighty! But what in heaven's name was that sound? It sounded as if it came from the churchyard. I'll get down there and check it out."

As Kavanagh hurriedly left the house, he shouted back to Brigid. "And get ready to call the doctor . . . or an ambulance. We may need them both."

The churchyard laid not five hundred meters from Kavanagh's house; a distance he covered at top speed. As he approached the church's iron gate, he swept his torch in a wide arc. Except for the men's unattended Range Rover, the torchlight showed the road ahead to be empty. Panting, he slowed to a walk and approached the open churchyard gate. Above him in the skies, the birds had vanished and now the air about him was suddenly heavy, leaden and silent.

"Hello there! . . . Mr. O'Carroll! . . . Mr.McCarthy? Are you there? Is everything all right in there?"

From within the churchyard walls, a whimpering sound greeted his call. Nervously, Kavanagh moved towards the sound; his flashlight seeking the source of the disturbing cries. The probing beam fell on a hunched figure huddled by the graveyard wall.

Kavanagh froze at the sight that assailed his eyes.

"Mr. McCarthy? . . . is that you? Are you all right? What in heaven's name happened here?" Kavanagh cautiously approached the hunched figure. As he neared, McCarthy clutched and clawed at the nearby wall and retreated further from the light.

"No! . . . no! . . . God save me! . . . save me! Christ! Don't let it near me. Oh! Jesus! . . . NO! NO! . . ." A terrified McCarthy covered his face with bloodstained hands.

"Joe! Joe! It's all right! . . . take it easy now! . . . It's me . . . Jack Kavanagh! God almighty man . . . you're covered in blood! What in God's name happened here?"

Clutching at the clinging ivy on the graveyard wall, Joe McCarthy stared a mad stare in Kavanagh's direction and continued to whimper while attempting to crawl away from the flashlight beam.

His choked sobs chilled Kavanagh to the bone.

"Joe! Joe! It's OK, Joe . . . steady on, man! Listen to me . . . you're safe now. Take it easy! Where's Mr. O'Carroll? . . . Where's Phil? Jesus, Mary and Joseph! What on earth is going on here?" McCarthy's face was transfigured in terror and his eyes spun wildly in his head.

"No! No! Merciful God! Don't let it get me! . . . don't let it get me! I told him . . . I warned Phil . . . but he wouldn't listen! . . . oh dear Jesus! Its eyes! Its eyes! . . . It came from hell itself! . . . and it's got Phil!! Save me! Sweet Jesus! Save me!"

"Oh my God! Where's O'Carroll?" A cold, new fear now joined panic in Kavanagh's heaving breast. " Mr.O'Carroll! . . . Phil!!! . . . are you there? . . . are you OK? . . . answer me! . . . are you there?"

He turned his torch in the direction of the church wall.

"Christ, I'd better locate O'Carroll. He could be injured."

Stumbling over the uneven tufted ground, Kavanagh moved

forward between tipsy gravestones and the church wall.

As he rounded the corner, his torch beam fell on a steel ladder propped up against the south wall. His heart pounding a steady tattoo against his ribcage, he gingerly picked his steps between the graves to the base of the ladder.

"Aaaagh!" He jumped at this terrifying sound. This time the scream had escaped from his lips. His eyes and torchlight beam settled on the still form of Phil O'Carroll, half-lying. half-seated by the church-door.

At that moment, the pale moon sneaked out from behind a canopy of cloud to cast a cold dim light on the open doorway and the figure slumped beneath it. Kavanagh staggered, then gagged, at the sight which his eyes now beheld.

It was O'Carroll all right but his features had completely altered. His staring, sightless eyes bulged – locked and frozen as if in the grip of some terrible horror – and his lips were drawn back to reveal a frozen, clenched-teeth grimace. Thick, dark lifeblood covered his face and his entire front.

It was obvious that Phil O'Carroll was dead; his neck ripped open as if by some savage animal. Kavanagh recoiled from the sight; yet he could not take his eyes from it. Again his heart pounded and banged in his chest, but try as he might, he could not move or avert his eyes.

For what seemed like an eternity, living eyes locked with those of the dead.

"Owwooo!"

The sound of an animal howling nearby snapped his mind back to the reality of the moment. In a fresh wave of panic, he swept his light left and right of the gloomy church entrance. He brought the beam finally to rest on the carved figure of the Sheela-na-Gig above the arched doorway.

There sat the old Stone Goddess – as she had done for centuries – Keeper of Secrets too terrible to be known or uttered – Her misshapen legs apart, Her shadowy, timeless face immobile in the pale moonlight.

Kavanagh gasped as his torchlight settled on Her secretive, stone features. For an instant, it seemed as if the Sheela's eyes came alive and blazed with such demonic fury such as he had never encountered before. He desperately tried to tear his eyes from Her piercing, hypnotic gaze and dropped to his knees and crossed himself. Jack Kavanagh's eyes then beheld a sight that would haunt him for the remainder of his days.

There, dripping from Her full, stone lips, was blood – fresh, human blood.

The moon withdrew behind a cloud and somewhere in the darkness, this time, a little further away; a dog – though it sounded to Kavanagh like the baying of a She-wolf – howled a single, long, unearthly howl.

The Piper in the Ring

He sat inside the magic Ring,
fingers sparkling on a wand of black,
and the music that he made that day
told a tale as old as creation.
An ancient tale
of bones and bloom, a language
of flesh and of roses.
A tale so old, the hills around
moved and bent to listen;
and did Spring's heart, hidden,
skip a beat
as the piper played 'The Blackbird'?

Ivory glinting in the May morning sun,
leather bellows breathing
life to bitter-sweet reeds.
Soul-stained tongues that sigh
and drip with nectar.
All Nature hushed and silenced
as She paused,
listening to her own sad
sweet eternal song.

Then the slumbering Hosts with the Ring
came awake in a shower of sound.
What piper plays?
A child of Theirs?
I trembled, for I watched Them dance
to music not for mortal ears.

I saw Them dance, while the piper played,
to Air and Earth and Ether,
I saw Them dance to Fire and Wind.

No Pipes of Pan ever played so sad
as the chanter's song that day.
No Siren's song could haunt my heart
as the tunes that he did play.
And the lyres and harps
beyond the Spheres
were silenced then for ever.
And did those Spheres
for an instant, dissolve,
awash in a flood of ancient tones?
Or was it all an old, old dream?
As the piper played 'The Blackbird'.

Dedicated to Paddy Keenan – Uilleann Piper

Beyond Moyasta Junction

A Ride On The West Clare Railway

IT WAS LIKE NO OTHER SOUND I HAD EVER heard before that moment and it stopped me dead in my tracks. From high out of the sky it came – long, piercing and mournful – like some banshee wail – which swooped unexpectedly from the frosty air to wash over and silence me at my play underneath the barren apple trees in the orchard in front of our house.

It silenced too the unharmonious, though familiar, farm-yard chorus of lowing cows, cackling geese and hens, gobbling turkeys and barking dogs. This was the early winter of 1950 and I was, at six years of age, by now well accustomed to the sounds of regular farmyard animals and the day and night cries of all manner of summer and winter birds. But here was a sound I had not before encountered – and it scared me.

In terror and in tears, I ran towards my mother as she returned from hanging out washing on the clothesline. "Its all right", she laughed. "There's no need to be frightened . . . 'tis only the 'West Clare', pulling into Corofin!"

"What's a 'West Clare'?" I asked, calmed now and anxious to learn what manner of extraordinary bird or beast could utter such a strange sound and why I had never heard it before this day.

"It's a train! . . . the West Clare train . . . whistling its arrival and we can hear it because the wind is from the south this morning. Shush now! Listen"

We faced south and cocked our ears to the bitter, clear air; but the rolling wave of sound had passed over us to reverberate and echo against the first high ridge of Burren rock it would encounter a mile or so north of our house.

"Its only the train . . . arrived in Corofin . . . on its way from Ennis to Kilrush. Maybe when your older and bigger we can take the West Clare back to Ennistymon to visit Mother . . . or Lahinch to see the sea . . . or even to Kilrush to see your Aunt and cousins"

'Mother', my grandmother, lived in Ennistymon – then the very edge of my known universe – and I had already accompanied my mother there for our annual Christmas-time visit in a local hackney car – then the only motorised transport available to us – hired for the day. Now there was the promise of a journey there again, this time aboard this strange contraption, which made such a terrifying sound. I was alight with both excitement and fear at the prospect of finally coming face to face with this mysterious 'West Clare' train.

In the weeks that followed, I must have plagued my mother with questions about the 'West Clare'.

What did a 'train' look like? Why and how did it make such a sound? Patiently, she described, as best she could, the gleaming engine and smokestack and the iron rail-tracks it rode on as it sped across the land from city to town, from village to village. She usually finished her description with a verse of the song, 'Are Ye Right There Michael, Are Ye Right!' (Written in 1912 by Percy French in gentle revenge; following the West Clare's failure to deliver him in time to lecture to a waiting audience in Kilkee.)

"Are ye right there Michael, are ye right?
Do you think that that we'll be there before the night?
Oh we've been so long in starting'
that ye couldn't say for sartin'
Still ye might now Michael, so ye might!"

I listened to my mother's song in awed silence. I tried to imagine what 'rail-tracks' might look like. I could not. Running not three miles south of our house was a set of rail-tracks I had never seen and which carried a train so famous that it had a song written about it.

I was utterly enchanted and captivated by the mystery of it all and my imagination grappled to cope with the concept of the physical proportions of this great and famous train as described to me in words, and song, by my mother.

My enthusiasm and constant questioning must have been well noted. On the following Christmas Morning, there, (courtesy of Santa Claus) to my amazement and delight, lying by the dying embers of an open peat-turf fire, along with presents for my brothers and sister, was a train-set; complete with painted engine, carriages, tracks and signals.

Obsessed as I was with my new toy, I knew now I just had to witness and experience the real thing. I just had to see, or better still, take a trip aboard this fabulous West Clare Train to any of its stopping points – Ennistymon, Lahinch, Miltown Malbay or Quilty – on its meandering, 17-stop, 53 mile journey from Ennis to distant Kilrush and Kilkee.

I must have pestered my father too with questions about the nature of this 'West Clare Train'. As I never again heard her whistle-wail as clearly as I had on that still, crisp winter's morning, and wondered aloud why this should be.

"The wind is from the west", was his curt, enigmatic reply to my questioning.

At last the day arrived when I would finally see for myself the source of the sound that I now longed, with all my heart, to hear up close. Every few months or do, my father would tackle up Molly, the horse, to the cart to go the three miles to the train station in Corofin to collect items of hardware ordered by my mother for our little country-shop from a Wholesaler in Limerick. Tin buckets and zinc basins; timber shovel and broom handles; hammers, hay forks, rakes and binder-twine; tins of paints, cans of oils; Tilley lamps and sometimes lengths of iron and horse-shoe nails for my father's forge . . . all were ultimately delivered on order on the West Clare train to the Railway Station a short distance outside the village of Corofin. In the absence of any other ways or means of delivery, a horse-and-cart excursion to the station was necessary to collect these items and I had – after much pleading and petitioning – been promised to be allowed to accompany my father on the very next trip.

I counted the hours till at last, the day arrived and then, having set off on our journey propped alongside my father on the horse-cart, I counted each hoof-clop of Molly's patient three-mile journey to the station. We arrived at last to find a gathering of other horse-and-cart teams – some private and some 'official' Carters; – whose job it was, in the absence of buses or delivery trucks, to meet the daily trains to collect and distribute – for a fare – all manner of goods to the village shops. I didn't realise it then, but this West Clare Train was famous – indeed infamous – for its tardy timekeeping. Now the dour drivers stood about the station yard smoking and talking and, along with the uniformed Station-Master, occasionally consulted pocket – watches, while awaiting the now long-overdue arrival of the celebrated train.

"She's comin', boys!" the Station Master at last called to nobody in particular. I moved to the edge of the platform and peered down the tracks into the misty distance.

There was nothing yet to be seen. Suddenly, another sound I had never heard before assailed my ears. From the silver-shined railway tracks beneath my feet a zinging, humming, metallic drone wafted up to assail my ears. The high-pitched hum exactly matching my own state of high tension and excitement at the sights and sounds I was soon to witness. Firstly came the longed-for whistle wail – even louder than I had imagined. Then, from out of the morning drizzle and mist, dreamlike and suspended in time and in space, the train itself appeared. Rattling, swaying and puffing like some drunken, hissing dragon, it slowly approached the platform and halted amid a screen of white steam and black coal smoke.

It was a sight I will never forget.

Here at last, close enough for me to reach out and to touch, in all her creaking, grumbling glory was the object of my boyhood fascination – the mythical 'West Clare' herself!

My memories of what followed are jumbled; such was the bustle of activity on the platform and my excitement and frantic desire to fully appreciate the Great Iron Spectacle which now trembled, heaved and sighed before my eyes; now smarting from the thick fog of coal-smoke which swirled about the black engine. I stared in awe at the engine (in fact, a medium-sized locomotive designed for narrow – gauge track – as was the West Clare Railway line), attached to two passenger carriages and a trailing Guard's van; from which poured all manner of parceled treasures which were immediately pounced upon by the waiting carters; including my father.

"Stand well back from the edge, now!" He directed at me while sifting through the growing hillock of bulging canvas bags, packages and boxes building up on the platform. "I don't want to have to bring you home in one of these sacks!"

All too soon, the van's contents, and a few heavily clad, package-laden passengers, are at last safely deposited on the platform. The Station-Master hands over a mysterious baton-stick to the Engine Driver and with a wave of a flag, a short toot on his whistle and shouts a loud salute, "Cheerio now and safe journey!"

Moving reluctantly away from its moorings amid more white steam emissions and the groaning and complaining of straining metal, the mighty West Clare shudders into rumbling life and – its rear end waggling like some grotesque metal duck – chugs sluggishly towards its next stop down the line to the west.

It is an image which haunts me still. While my father calmed a panicked Molly and loaded the cart with assorted hardware, I stood on the platform-edge and gazed at the tail-end of the train as it waggled off into a tunnel of gray mist to disappear at last from my world; a world which – because of its coming to this small rural halting-station – had now changed for ever.

From out of the mist, came a single long, lonesome whistle wail followed by two shorter whelps as the train chugged westward. This was followed by a great silence and a sense of emptiness all around.

In the fleet years that followed, I witnessed the arrival and departure of the 'West Clare' on many occasions; both as my father's helper on those regular trips to collect goods and later, (when considered old and able enough for such responsible missions) as sole commander of Molly and the cart. In the meantime, I conducted a constant and committed lobbying of my mother to be allowed to take a trip on this fantastical machine. She obviously must have relented to my pleading, because, one afternoon in early August, I found myself standing alone on the platform of the Corofin Station, a lad of ten, decked out in my Sunday clothes clutching a small suitcase and waiting, on this occasion, not to collect goods for our shop, but to embark on my first-ever train journey to visit my Aunt and cousins in distant Kilrush. I could hardly contain my excitement.

At last, I was to be an actual passenger, a train – traveller; one of those shadowy figures I had so many times before glanced briefly through white steam, black smoke and dirty carriage windows.

"I see you're travelling today? And a lovely day it is too for a train-journey." The Stationmaster beamed as I proudly purchased a return second-class ticket for this long-awaited, epic journey.

"So you're off to Kilrush! That's beyond Moyasta, you know!"

I knew of Moyasta; my mother had warned me of a possible change of trains at this far-flung railway outpost. I feared complications.

"Will I have to change trains at Moyasta?" I timidly inquired.

"You'll have to change at Moyasta Junction. Otherwise you'll end up in Kilkee." The Stationmaster beamed down at me, while again consulting the fob-watch adorning his blue uniform tunic jacket.

I went out and stood on the platform-edge, nervously gazing down the rail-lines. Maybe today – I panicked at the thought – maybe today, the West Clare just might not make it. Finally, the silver ribbons of wheel-polished track beneath my feet 'zinged' the news that she was indeed on her way. After what seemed like an eternity of waiting, the West Clare finally arrived – late as usual.

Soon I was aboard, my suitcase tucked away on the overhead net-rack, and settled in one of the small 6-person compartments. My travelling companions for my first trip silently examined the latest arrival to their encapsulated world. Seated next to me was a stout woman surrounded by a great number of large parcels wrapped in brown paper (too bulky and weighty to store in the overhead rack); a farmer, with a canvas bag from which poked the head of a kid-goat, and a tall Black man – the first I had ever seen in my life.

The train had travelled but a few miles, when it slowed and – as it passed through a level crossing with brightly painted gates – a package was tossed from the Guard's van into a pair of waiting hands. More than once on that journey, without the train actually coming to a halt, similar unscheduled deliveries were made (newspapers, assorted packages and other sundries purchased in far-off Ennis) to beaming, waving men and women waiting at level crossings or an a track-side moot. (This practice seemingly was a long- established daily event on the train-journey to and from Kilrush – a side of home-cured bacon delivered to Mrs. Kearns; a leg of lamb to Mrs. Reilly; a live goose to Mrs. O'Brien; day-old chicks to Mrs. Burke or a Plow-share to Jack Daly.)

As the train approached Ennistymon through a tunnel of swirling steam, I was startled once again at the sheer volume of the steam-whistle as the Driver signaled his imminent arrival in the town. (I was to hear a similar sound again, 30 years later, in central China as our massive steam-locomotive powered train crossed the mighty Yellow River at dawn; on a train journey from Beijing to Xian). A horse and her foal in a nearby field – nostrils flared and tails cocked behind them – galloped frantically to a far corner of the field to distance themselves from this rattling, rolling, wailing iron-horse which had invaded their domain.

At Ennistymon Station, I peered through the window fogged in a veil of smoke and engine-steam to witness the bustle and excitement of loading and unloading both passengers and cargo, raking the engine-fires and loading coal for the ongoing journey. Beneath us lay the old village of Ennistymon, still and sleepy on this lazy summer day. At last the Stationmaster's flag signals time to depart.

Two miles west, after yet another short stop at Lahinch Station, offering passengers a tantalising bird's-eye view of the seaside resort's famed horse-shoe golden beach, the train swung left on a course for its next stop some five miles down the line at Miltown Malbay. From Lahinch it rocks and rolls directly south towards the townland of Rineen; where, on the 22nd October 1920, local soldiers of the Old IRA ambushed a despised Black and Tan patrol lorry; killing four and seriously injuring one other soldier.

Further south and to our left, a host of tiny thatched, white-washed cottages stood as if randomly dotted about on a patchwork quilt of fields, gardens and meadows; now brimming over with the fruits of summers labours. A mile or so further south of Rineen the track again veers left and south-east to take us into the imposing Station House at Miltown Malbay; all the while the sunlight keeping pace; all the while dancing on the glittering Atlantic seascape to our right and spotlighting the ever-nearing church steeple which dominated this cozy, West Clare coastal hamlet.

Now, in high summer, the seascape panorama to our right as we travel south looks positively Mediterranean, serene and inviting. In winter however, this rugged sea and landscape underwent a change of personality. It became, in the words of one writer, "One of the most savage, storm-swept coasts in all of Europe."

Today the sea smiles benignly and dances playfully as we trundle along; giving us its best views of empty golden beach and Liscannor; birthplace of John Philip Holland, inventor of the submarine.

Further to the northwest, we have views of Hags Head and some distance out to sea, the Aran Islands – the last solid ground before the New World. Further down the coast to the south lay Spanish Point; where in the winter of 1588, six Galleons of the great Armada from King Philip's Spain met a watery end on this cruel, jagged shore.

At the station at Miltown Malbay we halted again and here two passengers -the taciturn farmer and his kid-goat – alighted.

Soon we were once again in motion. I was beside myself with excitement. Now aboard the train, no longer content to be just a 'passenger', I now longed to be both up front with the Engine Driver and Fireman and trailing behind in the Guard's van. I felt as if I never wanted to be anywhere other than be aboard this rattling, swaying train as it snaked past the villages of Quilty, Annagh, Kilmurry, Gragganock, Doonbeg and Shragh on its way to the famed Moyasta Junction.

Seated opposite me, on the button-studded, well-worn carriage -seat, the Black man spoke for the first and only time on the trip.

"New York . . . and Boston . . ." He caught my eye, then nodded towards the ocean. "Waaay over . . . in that direction!"

He, and I, continued to stare in silence at the ocean and in the direction of Boston until – south of Quilty – the train veered inland and the sparkling sea fell away at last as we plunged deeper into the patchwork of emerald grazing pastures, kitchen gardens, peat-bogs pockmarked with reeks of turf, rushy meadows and, further to the east, the barren expanse of Mount Callan.

All too soon, the train pulled into Moyasta Junction in a light summer drizzle. Here, at this small rural station-house and platform, I and the Black man gathered our belongings from the webbed overhead, luggage rack, nodded our 'goodbyes' to the stout woman (who uttered not a single word throughout the entire journey) and stepped down from the train and on to the deserted triangular platform.

Happily, I only had to cross the gravel v-shaped platform to board the single-carriage connecting train waiting to ferry a handful of local passengers – already aboard the train – to Kilrush. As the train chugged out of Moyasta for the last leg of our journey to the terminus at Kilrush, I caught one last glimpse of my exotic-looking travelling companion – this tall African man – standing alone on a bleak and windswept rural railway – platform in West Clare waiting; for whom, or for what, I could only surmise.

All too soon, with a final wail of whistle and squeal of brakes, the train, having followed the shining expanse and contours of the mighty Shannon River, came to its final halt in Kilrush. Now, just over two hours since I boarded in distant Corofin, I reluctantly collect my case and climb down from the train to be greeted excitedly by my cousins.

Though the magic spell of my long journey was broken, I felt proud and happy. Proud that I had completed my first solo journey away from home and happy that I had finally achieved my long-held dream to ride this famous steam-driven train on the West Clare Railway.

In the years between then and now, I continued my love affair with trains and train travel. Once aboard a train, one enters a very civilised, often romantic, mode of transport. It's a very special world, a unique, encapsulated world, a sort of time-bubble of rhythm and movement capable of both hypnotising and enchanting the traveller. Once aboard, the traveller may shed the cares, woes and worries of the world outside and give himself, or herself, to a subtle magic which can be woven by even the most mundane of train journeys. It is my belief that people are altered in some way by train travel. Personalities change; masks and personas are discarded as the world outside slips gently by to a backdrop of metallic, though extremely melodic, conversation between steel-wheel and steel-rail.

I have been fortunate enough in my life to undertake several memorable train journeys. In Malaya, from Kuala Lumpur to

Singapore; across Central China from Beijing to Chungdu and in the USA, from New Orleans to Los Angeles.

On each and every trip, I experience the self-same emotions as I did on my first journey all those years ago; the excitement in anticipation of the journey; the heightened sense of awareness once aboard the train and the strange and inexplicable sense of loss and loneliness at journey's end.

"To travel hopefully," wrote Robert Louis Stevenson, "is a better thing than to arrive."

I suspect that Stevenson must have, like me, harboured a great and undying passion for all manners, shapes and sizes of trains and the sheer, unadulterated romance of train travel. Be they journeys yet to be undertaken on the Orient Express or the Trans-Siberian railway; journeys already taken, across the central Chinese Plains, across the vast, empty American Prairies or my first, never-to-be-forgotten steam-train journey to Kilrush, via Moyasta Junction, on the great West Clare Railway.

Note: Using a Silver Spade and special wheelbarrow, Charles Stuart Parnell (MP) turned the first sod of the West Clare railway in Ennis on the 26th. January 1885. The completed line eventually opened for passenger traffic on 23rd December 1893.

On 31st January 1961, in keeping with the national transport policy of the time, the Golden Age of the West Clare Railway – after 68 years of daily passenger and freight service – came to an ignominious end with the closing of the line; the single-gauge track dismantled and its rolling stock sold to Kenya.

A great and Golden Age of train travel in Clare had come to an end.

The Day
the Music Died

THE "DASHER" LOOKED REALLY PEEVED AS I rounded the corner of the town square, red-faced, breathless and laden down with schoolbag, hurley and muddy football boots. "Bloody hell! Callan, I've sprouted a bloody moustache waiting for you. What the bleedin' hell kept ya?" He hunched his shoulders, adopted his best James Dean pose and peered from beneath a shock of fair hair.

"Brother Galvin held me back after class." I gulped, "Bloody Inter. Cert. Geometry, I'll never get the hang of it."

The Dasher squinted, "Who needs geometry and screw Galvin, and the rest of the hoors from Hell." A look of fear flickered for a moment in his eyes; "Galvin! He's a bloody sadist, a reject from the S.S. so the cousin says. He says he's got a Swastika tattooed on his arse. That's why he keeps scratching it."

We both laughed, nervously looked about us, and started to walk towards Lane's newsagents and sweet shop. "Anyway, we can forget about the mad bastard 'till the morning. How much you got on you?" The Dasher jingled some loose change in his pocket. "Enough for munchies?"

"No way, I got munchies last time, and anyway I'm saving what I got for the juke box."

"Oh yeehh! Awopbopaloobop! . . . rip it up! . . . an' great balls of fire! You an' that bloody jukebox. I'm almost skint . . . hey, lend me a shilling and tonight that Kitty Leyden will be mine, I tell you, all mine!"

The Dasher did a jive and twirl, put on what he thought was his Elvis pout and paid Mrs. Lane for a bag of Licorice Allsorts, Beano and Topper comics and five Woodbine cigarettes. Mrs. Lane "tut-tutted" as the Dasher went into his best Humphrey Bogart routine. "Thanksh shweethaard!" he winked at her through hooded eyes and pushed a handful of Allsorts into his mouth.

"C'mon, podner! Lets git outta this one-horse town." He munched and offered the paper-bag to me. "Jeez, I'm gaspin' for a ciggy." Mrs. Lane shook her head and glared at her customer,

"Young David Dalton, smokin' and swearin' and givin' aul' guff at your age. Your poor mother should hear you . . . you'll come to no good . . . or end up in Piccadilly, mark my words."

"I hope so, Mrs. Lane, I hope so!" The Dasher and I departed the shop laughing; stuffing our faces as we went.

A cold wind whipped down the near-empty street and licked our cheeks with a light early February drizzle. "Are you heading home, Dash?" I inquired.

"No bloody way! The Ma is there on her own. If I poke my nose in she won't let me out again. Same bloody story every day." The Dasher looked up and down the street and gave a long sigh. "God! But I can't wait to get the fuck outta this hick town. Roll on the bloody Leaving in '61. My God! That's two years yet . . . but then! . . . taaraa! taaraa!" He trumpeted at the gray sky, "then it's bye-bye ma, bye-bye sis and a big byesy-bye to Brother 'Adolph' Galvin and the rest of his blitzkrieg unchristian Brethren and hello Broadway!. . . maybe Hollywood even".

He went into his James Dean pose again and asked, running his fingers through his hair. "What'cha think?", he turned to me, "'Ya think I might make it in Hollywood? a James Dean part maybe?"

He always asked this, wanting me to say yes and tell him how much he looked like Dean, which sometimes I did to humour him. Trouble was – I had to grudgingly admit to myself – he did look a lot like Dean, though I always figured he looked more like Eddie Cochran; which never seemed to impress him.

"Make it in Hollywood? You wouldn't make it in . . . in Hollyhead. You! A James Dean! You look more like Charlie flipping Chan than James Dean."

"Your just jealous, is what you are." The Dasher sneered.

"Kitty Leyden told me I'd be the spit of Dean if I had a snazzy red bomber-jacket just like the one he wore in 'Rebel Without a Cause'. She's crazy about me, you know. I've written to the brother in New York to send me one . . . then watch Miss Kitty-Kat Leyden purr!"

"You!" I snorted through my allsorts, "turn into James Dean when you get a red bomber-jacket? You couldn't turn into Dean if your brother sent you a red bomber aircraft. Stick to Charlie Chan, Dash. There was only one Dean, and he's dead. And as for Kitty being crazy about you!! . . . She's got more taste . . . else she's just plain crazy!"

The Dasher looked hurt for a moment then squelched up his face and spat out; "Dean's not dead. That's just Hollywood publicity. How could Dean be dead? It's Charlie bloody Chan that's dead. Anyway, I'd rather look like a Charlie Chan than your mate 'Bloody' Holly! I bet Dean could sing too. If he had wanted to, he could've been, should've been the real 'King of Rock 'n Roll'. Boy! That'd be really something, James Dean singing 'Heartbreak Hotel', and 'All Shook Up'. Anyway, Holly doesn't sing . . . he hiccups!"

Now the Dasher had ventured onto sacred ground. He did this to rise me and it worked every time. I reddened and went into defence.

"What do you know! You thought Fats Domino was a board game and Jerry Lee played left-back for Tipperary 'till I put you right. You wouldn't recognise Elvis if he came and sat next to you in class in the morning. Let me tell you some Rock 'n Roll facts, you pitiful ignoramus. Buddy Holly is the real 'King of Rock 'n Roll' . . . he's a genius . . . writes his own songs, has his own group, makes his own records, plays his own solos . . . on a Fender Stratocaster!" I paused to see if the Dasher had taken in this important item of information, "and . . ." I added with a sneer, "he's only 21 . . . the same age as your stupid brother in New York . . . who's only a chippy!"

"Yeah! So bloody what! Holly looks like the geek who gets the sand kicked in his face in the Charles Atlas advert. Come to think of it, with those glasses, you look a lot like him".

"Who, Holly?" I asked, hopefully.

"Naaaa! The bloody seven-stone loser geek in those ads. You still have the sand in your hair and it's clouding up your geeky specs." He reached to brush invisible sand from my hair. I blushed and turned into the driving wind. I hated these new wire-rimmed glasses. Nobody 'cool' wore glasses. Only swats wore glasses and I was no swat. Elvis didn't wear glasses, neither did Don or Phil. But Buddy Holly did and I figured he probably used them to be different or needs them because of all those ace songs he's written. If I could write just one of those songs, or play guitar like him, then these geek glasses wouldn't be so bad. In the meantime, I wished I could fling them into the nearest dustbin.

I decided to change the subject. "Are we going to Kelly's Café or not? They might have some new Rock 'n Roll records in the jukebox."

"All right! all right! . . . stay cool man, we'll get there." The Dasher pushed a hand deep into a pocket, "But first I just have to have a drag of this ciggy or I'll burst. C'mon, let's go to Jack's."

A wrecked car at the back of Jack's Garage was a favourite stop for the Dasher between school and Kelly's Café. There, with the Dasher at the wheel and me stretched out in the back seat, we would smoke two of the five Woodbine cigarettes while discussing the important topics of the day. How would the intrepid space explorer Colonel Dan Dare – Pilot of the Future – get out of the tight spot he and his side-kick Digby found themselves in as prisoners of the dreaded alien Mekon? Was Roy of the Rovers really Christy Ring's English cousin? Who was the better looking . . . Rita Conlan or Kitty Leyden? . . . and was Elvis really a hermaphrodite? The Dasher, who had looked up the word in his dictionary, reckoned he was.

"Did you ever notice how smooth his face looks in those photos? Smooth as a baby's bottom it is! And his hair! For sure, he's a hermo . . . herma . . . hermopodike or whatever the heck you call those weirdos. Same as that ponce Fabian, and I have my doubts about Cliff too."

"Cliff Richard!" I shook my head," Naaaa! Fabian maybe, but not Cliff. C'mon Dash," I stubbed out my Woodbine in the overflowing car ashtray, "It's getting late . . . lets get to Kelly's."

"Yeah, Ok, Ok, I know you gotta have your dose of Holly hiccups or you'll go into serious spasm. Anyway, maybe little Miss Kitty-Kat will be there and . . ." He nudged me as we scrambled from the old MG, "maybe even Rita the Raver! C'mon, kiddo . . . race you there."

Coming through the door of Kelly's Café we could see it was

146

busy, as usual. I wiped the condensation from my glasses and looked around the café. 'Matso' McMahon and 'Pedro' Sullivan from our class were at a table engaged in deep conversation with two first-year Convent girls. The Dasher called to them, but they ignored him.

"Feck them! . . . can't stand the competition. A coke and a Tizer and a bag of chips, he's paying". He shouted at Mrs. Kelly and pointed at me. My attention had shifted to the other end of the room. Above the hubbub of cafe-conversation came an instantly recognisable sound. From the Seeburg Jukebox at the far end of the café came an unmistakable sound.

It was the voice of Buddy Holly singing 'Everyday'.

"They must've seen you coming", the Dasher said as we moved to a vacant table near the window, "They're playing your main man. Hey, look! There's Rita and Kitty."

He waved at the two girls across the room, huddled in what seemed like a serious conversation. They too ignored his greeting.

"Hmmmph! Stuck up cows!"

The Dasher swallowed his last licorice Allsort and followed it with a handful of steaming chips. I watched Rita go to the juke-box and feed it with change. The machine whirled; the Bakelite robot-arm moved and selected a 45 single disc from the spinning carousal and, with one, quick, smooth action, delivered it to the turntable.

It was Buddy Holly singing 'Everyday'. I smiled at the Dasher who shrugged. The song finished and the jukebox whirled and once again delivered the same disc onto the turntable. Again it was Holly's 'Everyday'.

"Buddy Holly! . . . again! . . . with the same bloody song", The Dasher glared across at the girl's table, "Whassamatter with those dotty dames."

"They have taste, Dash," I said; though I was disappointed. "But they should've gone for the A side, 'Peggy Sue' . . . on the Coral label. That's dynamite! A killer! He plays the Electric guitar solo, you know. 'Everyday' is not Rock 'n Roll . . . too soft."

"Yeah, typical! Those soppy dames going for the slushy, lovey-dovey stuff. Get up there, Callan . . . before they get anymore loot in the box . . . and while you're up there, see if they have any James Dean singles? . . . lets hear some REAL Rock 'n Roll!"

I laughed and dug deep in my pocket for the single shilling I had saved to feed this demanding Jukebox. From the corner of my eye I saw Rita glaring at us from across the room. They were still huddled together in deep conversation then Kitty picked up a newspaper, stood up, crossed to our table and stood over us.

"You're the last one I expected to be laughing, after . . ." She looked angry and seemed to be blinking back a tear, ". . . after what's happened."

"What are you talking about? What happened?" the Dasher looked at her as if she was some deranged person.

I looked at the headline in big, bold typeface. In utter amazement, I read the bold headline and the small print underneath ˆ

"TOP 'ROCK' STARS DIE IN CRASH"

"Three of America's top Rock 'n Roll stars were killed in a plane crash early today, a few hours after delighting teenagers at a 'big beat' Concert. The dead included Buddy Holly, . . ."

The DEAD . . . included . . . **BUDDY . . . HOLLY!** . . . I froze, my eyes refusing to continue or accept the words I had just read. An image of a smiling Buddy, in his white suit and holding his red Fender Strat, floated before my eyes.

I forced my eyes back to the page and commanded them reread this unbelievable headline. Though it floated in and out of focus, it still read the same.

The names screamed from the page.

Buddy Holly, Ritchie Valens and The Big Bopper killed in a plane crash near Clear Lake, Iowa.

No! I shook my head, no! . . . this is not for real! This had to be some sort of joke, a bloody bad joke too. Buddy Holly, dead! Buddy was unique, special, a genius! . . . he just couldn't be dead. This had to be wrong. Death didn't happen to stars like Buddy. I stared at Kitty and waited for her to tell us it was all just a gag, some huge early April Fool's joke.

Tugging nervously at her ponytail she was gushing and stammering, explaining to the Dasher, ". . . It's all over all the papers, and even on the half-one news on the radio. Everyone knows about it. The whole world knows. Where have you two been?"

"Buddy Holly? THE Buddy Holly?" the Dasher repeated the name slowly, "dead!"

"Well," he smirked and peered at me, "it cured his hiccups, I suppose."

"Don't be so bloody smart, Dash! . . . Can't you see he's upset." Kitty sat down next to me and gently touched my arm, "Buddy was great! 'Everyday' is dreamy . . . he seemed nice . . . he had a nice smile." She sniffed and reached for the handkerchief tucked up her sleeve.

The Dasher stared at the Jukebox, which was repeating 'Everyday', and said flatly, "Buddy Holly . . . dead! James Dean . . . dead! Buddy Holly and James Dean . . . Jesus Christ! Un-bloody-believable!"

He sat shaking his head.

Rita Conlan had joined us and sat down next to Kitty. "Ritchie Valens was my favourite, but I liked Buddy too" she said gently and stared with us in silence at the jukebox. Buddy's voice was soft and sad as he sang.

"Everyday, it's a getting closer,
Going faster like a roller coaster."

Now, for the first time, I truly listened to the words and the sound of the song. I had never listened, really listened, like this, before this moment. Buddy sounded different somehow; in a way I had not heard or understood before. His voice caressed and flavoured the words of this beautiful love-song. Yet, he seemed lost and frightened as if he somehow knew his destiny and now he poured out his yearning and longing from this glowing box of dreams in the corner.

I rose, still dazed and confused, and moved to the Jukebox, fed the slot with my last shilling and returned to the table. The silky sound of Buddy's 'Everyday' once again washed over the café; now strangely silent.

We sat together for a long time without speaking. Buddy Holly was gone, but his music remained and which – around this cafe table – we now shared as a Communion.

Eventually, the Dasher threw his arm over my hunched shoulders and whispered,

"Hey, I was only foolin' you know. Holly was no geek. He was cool. He's just like Dean . . . with glasses! Holly and Dean! Dean and Holly! What a team, what a pair . . . they're not dead . . . not really!"

I nodded in agreement and smiled weakly and tried to hide the tears welling up in my eyes. I felt a huge, empty hole open up inside me. I stared through the café window as raindrops beat a solemn rhythm on the misted windowpane.

Even the sky was crying.

I glanced across the café table at Kitty, Rita and the Dasher; lost in their own thoughts. They looked different – older somehow. I felt older too. Much, much older in a way I could not yet fathom or explain.

I wished – as I never wished before – that I never had come into this café today, to hear this news, which – I knew in my heart – would change everything.

Note on Author

Born in the Burren, Co Clare, PJ Curtis is an award-winning broadcaster, record producer and writer. He has produced fifty four albums to date including two-times USA NAIRD Award-winning Altan, Maura O'Connell, Mary Black, Freddie White, Stocktons Wing, Davy Spillane, Dolores Keane, Mick Hanly, Ronan Leonard and Sean Tyrrell.

A recipient of a Hon M.A. 2005 (NUIG) and winner of three national awards for his radio programmes on RTE Radio 1, Century and Lyric FM, PJ has also had four books published to date: *'Notes From The Heart – A Celebration Of Irish Traditional Music'* (Poolbeg 1994) and a novel *'One Night In The Life of RV Mulrooney'* (Poolbeg 1996). *'The Music of Ghosts – A Burren Miscellany'* (Old Forge Books 2003.) *'The Lightning Tree'* (Brandon Books 2006)

Note on Photographer

Mike Mulcaire's work has been widely published in books, magazines, and post cards. His stylised images are also featured on corporate campaigns, CD covers and international media. Featured as one of six photographers who travelled the world, documenting the lives of Irish emigrants, in *'The Scattering'*, an award winning publication. Web address: mphotographx.com

Lightning Source UK Ltd.
Milton Keynes UK
20 August 2010

158755UK00001B/101/A

9 780954 536503